Croner's Guide to F

Croner's Guide to
Fire Safety

Colin S. Todd MSc, AI FireE, MSFPE, CEng, MIEE

Croner Publications Ltd
Croner House
London Road
Kingston upon Thames
Surrey KT2 6SR
Telephone: 081-547 3333

First Published 1992

Published by
Croner Publications Ltd,
Croner House,
London Road,
Kingston upon Thames,
Surrey KT2 6SR
Telephone: 081-547 3333

While every care has been taken
in the writing and editing of this book,
readers should be aware that only Acts of Parliament
and Statutory Instruments have the force of law,
and that only the courts can authoritatively
interpret the law

British Library Cataloguing in Publication Data
A CIP Catalogue Record for this book is available from
the British Library

ISBN 1-85524-088-2

Printed in Great Britain by
Whitstable Litho Printers Ltd, Whitstable, Kent

Contents

Acknowledgements

The author wishes to thank the following for assistance in the reviewing of specific chapters of the book:

Mr. A. Lewis, Fire Protection Association
Mr. B. Perry, Fire Protection Association
Mr. S. Ham, FiSEC
Dr. E. Marchant, Unit of Fire Safety Engineering, University of Edinburgh
Dr. D. Drysdale, Unit of Fire Safety Engineering, University of Edinburgh
Dr. K. Paul, RAPRA Technology Ltd
Mr. R. Ward, Control Risks Ltd
Mr. B. Kempster
Mr. A. Davis
Mr. A. Gatfield, Home Office Fire Service Inspectorate
Mr. R. Young, Loss Prevention Council
Mr. C. Mills
Mr. D. Boughen, Chubb Fire Engineering
Mr. R. Hammond, Concept Design
Mr. K. Skingle, Skingle Watson Partnership
Mr. D. Tidbury, C.S. Todd & Associates Ltd
Mr. R. Hirst

To Keith and Jayne

Introduction

Each year, despite the constant efforts of fire brigades, fire insurance companies, professional fire advisers and a plethora of other interested bodies, nearly 1000 people die in fires in the United Kingdom, while over 10,000 injuries occur due to fire. The majority of these fatal and non-fatal casualties occur in domestic premises, rather than places of work. The reasons for this include the enhanced risk of injury if fire occurs when people are asleep, the absence of legislative control over fire safety in most private dwellings and the absence of the very old and very young, both of whom are, statistically, high risk categories, from places of work. Nevertheless, a number of employees are killed or injured each year due to fire in their workplace. In addition, and often more memorably, members of the public are sometimes involved in very serious fire incidents as they shop, travel or engage in recreational activities. The need for fire precautions is, therefore, easily established, in most buildings.

Fire also results in serious economic losses. The most obvious of these is direct damage to property, which in 1990 resulted in record claims from insurance companies and for the first time exceeded, £1000 million. Even this figure takes no account of uninsured damage to property nor, more importantly, the indirect or consequential losses suffered by industry and commerce due to the loss of profits following a major fire. Although consequential loss (or "business interruption") can be insured, the effects of a serious fire on the future revenue earning of a business can be difficult to quantify. It is often claimed that a significant number of companies cease trading within a few years of a major fire. Undoubtedly, a large fire can result in loss of confidence by customers, long term loss of business and ultimately loss of jobs.

The management of fire risk and the engineering of fire safety measures is gradually becoming identified as a discipline in its own right. It is, however, a discipline that impinges on, and draws from, many other disciplines, including management science, building design, mechanical engineering, electrical engineering, chemical engineering, law, psychology, physics and chemistry. Fire-related legislation is subject to change; knowledge of fire behaviour in complex buildings is advancing and the facilities for formal education of practitioners in the field of fire safety are expanding.

The purpose of this book is to provide a basic guide to this complex subject for the non-specialist, such as the facilities manager, the personnel manager, the building manager, and others with responsibilities for fire safety in buildings. The approach adopted is to divide the subject into a number of discrete components, each of which is considered separately. The breadth of the topics discussed is such that it is not possible to consider any one topic in a depth beyond that required by the generalist. However, in each chapter, guidance is given on sources of further information for the reader with an interest in specialist aspects of the subject.

The division of fire safety into independent topics is necessary in a text book; it is not the manner in which fire safety should be approached in an actual building. For example, the absence of an automatic fire detection system in a relatively large building in which people sleep, might result in a low standard of fire safety. The absence of smoke stop doors in the long and convoluted corridors of the same building would, in itself, be considered unacceptable, as would the absence of emergency lighting. The overall effect of these three deficiencies is much greater than the simple sum of the individual deficiencies; a fire during the night may develop, undetected, until the corridors are completely smoke logged, so that means of escape are impassable and, in any case, difficult to use because the normal lighting has failed due to fire damage to the cables of the lighting circuits. Many fire disasters have arisen from an unfortunate combination of apparently independent defects, any one of which, if rectified, would have ameliorated the situation in which those involved found themselves.

A corollary to the above assertion is that it may be possible to "trade off" one measure against another. This is already recognised to a limited extent by legislation and the manner in which it is enforced, but it is likely that in the future greater scope for this approach will be permitted. Already, Building Regulations recognise that sprinkler protection may, in certain cases, permit compartment sizes to be increased. In future it might be argued that, for example, the standard of enclosure afforded to an escape route to prevent ingress of fire and smoke may reasonably be reduced to some degree if automatic smoke detection were present in all areas adjacent to the escape route; if occupants are alerted early enough, they can escape before the (reduced) integrity of the enclosing construction is threatened by the fire.

Unfortunately, the assessment of such inter-relationships still remains something of an art rather than a science. Before departing from standard solutions, the reader is, therefore, advised to seek expert opinion and the views of enforcing authorities; the latter tend to be rather conservative in approach. Indeed, before specifying any fire protection measure of any real complexity, cost or effect on overall fire safety, early consultation with all interested parties, particularly those charged with enforcement of legislation and insurance of the property, is strongly advocated.

Further Reading

1. *Fire Statistics United Kingdom.* Published annually by the Home Office.

Chapter 1
Fire Safety Legislation

Historical Background

Historically, most fire safety legislation has arisen from specific fire disasters. For example, it is widely held that the Factories Act 1961 arose as a result of the fire at a mill in Keighley some five years before. Equally, it is said that the fire at Hendersons department store in Liverpool in 1960 gave rise to the fire safety requirements imposed by the Offices, Shops and Railway Premises Act 1963. Even the cornerstone of United Kingdom fire safety legislation, the Fire Precautions Act 1971, was said to be enacted as a result of 11 deaths in a fire at the Rose and Crown Hotel, Saffron Walden in 1969. In very recent times, the Fire Safety and Safety of Places of Sport Act followed the fire at Bradford football stadium in 1985, while the Fire Precautions (sub-surface railway stations) Regulations 1989 arose as a result of the fire at Kings Cross underground station in 1987.

This approach to the legislative control of fire safety has caused fire safety legislation to be piecemeal and fragmented, which it remains to some extent.

However, some attempts to consolidate the legislation followed from the recommendations of the Holroyd Report in 1970. The report recommended that fire safety legislation should be divided into two main branches; one dealing with new buildings, the other with occupied premises. This is largely the current situation. In England and Wales, new buildings and major alterations to existing buildings, are required to comply with the Building Regulations 1985. In Scotland, buildings must comply with the Building Standards (Scotland) Regulations 1990 and in Northern Ireland, with the Building Regulations (Northern Ireland) 1990. The Building Regulations are the responsibility of the Department of the Environment and are enforced by the building control officer of the local authority who consults with the fire authority on matters relating to fire safety.

Building Regulations 1985

The Building Regulations 1985 apply to virtually all new buildings and material alterations to existing buildings, in England and Wales. Certain types of the following buildings are exempt from control:

— buildings to which the Explosives Acts apply
— buildings on sites for which a licence under the Nuclear Installations Act is required
— ancient monuments
— agricultural buildings and greenhouses
— temporary buildings and mobile homes
— small detached buildings and detached buildings that would not normally be entered by people.

The Building Regulations require there to be adequate means of escape in case of fire. At present, this requirement applies only to offices, shops and buildings of three or more storeys that comprise a house or flats. Requirements for adequate means of escape in all buildings covered by the Regulations are proposed, and could well come into place during 1992.

The Regulations were produced under powers granted by the Building Act 1984, and are currently the subject of a major review by the Department of the Environment. However the current situation is as described below.

Fire safety is addressed by Part B of Schedule 1 to the Building Regulations. Part B is sub-divided into four parts: B1, B2, B3 and B4. B1 requires that, in certain classes of occupancy:

> There shall be means of escape in case of fire from the building to a place of safety outside the building capable of being safely and effectively used at all material times.

This requirement applies to:

(a) a building which is erected and which
   (i) is or contains a dwelling-house of three or more storeys
   (ii) contains a flat and is of three or more storeys
   (iii) is or contains an office or

(iv) is or contains a shop

(b) a dwelling-house which is extended or materially altered and will have three or more storeys, and

(c) a building of three or more storeys, the use of which is materially changed to use as a dwelling-house.

However, in the case of a dwelling-house or a flat, the means of escape requirement applies only to the occupants of the third storey or above. Similarly, in the case of a building that *contains* an office or shop, the means of escape is required only for the occupants of the office or shop.

Part B1

The requirement expressed in B1 can be satisfied only by complying with a document entitled *The Building Regulations 1985–Mandatory rules for means of escape in case of fire,* although relaxations may be granted. This document contains no technical requirements, except in the case of loft conversions in two storey dwelling houses. Instead, the mandatory rules require compliance with specified parts of BS 5588 (Fire precautions in the design and construction of buildings), as follows:

Dwelling-houses:	Section 1.1: 1984 (Code of practice for single family dwelling houses)
Shops:	Part 2: 1985 (Code of practice for shops)
Offices:	Part 3: 1983 (Code of practice for office buildings).

In the case of flats, the mandatory rules require compliance with specified clauses of British Standard Code of Practice CP3 (Code of basic data for the design of buildings, Chapter IV, Part 1).

It should be noted that BS 5588 Section 1.1 and CP3 Chapter IV Part 1 have now been replaced by a single document, BS 5588 Part 1: 1990 (Code of practice for residential buildings). Also, Parts 2 and 3 of BS 5588 have been subject to considerable amendment. However, technically, because the mandatory rules have not been amended, compliance with B1 of the Building Regulations will only require compliance with the original standards described above. It should also be noted that, after consultation with the fire authority, the local authority may relax technical requirements that emanate from the standards specified in the mandatory rules.

Rigid compliance with codes required by Part B1, contrasts completely with Parts B2, 3 and 4 which merely specify performance requirements rather than detailed technical requirements. This permits the designer greater flexibility. The contrast may, however, be short lived, as it is likely that one outcome of the current review will be the redrafting of B1 as a performance requirement.

Part B2

B2 is concerned with measures to restrict the spread of fire over internal surfaces, such as walls and ceilings. The requirement is that materials used on walls and ceilings must be adequately resistant to spread of flame over their surfaces and, in some cases, that, if ignited, the rate of heat release will not be excessive.

Part B3

B3 is concerned with measures to limit the spread of fire within the building and to prevent structural collapse due to fire. It requires that, in the event of fire:

- the building will remain stable for a "reasonable period"
- large buildings be sub-divided into fire resisting compartments
- concealed spaces be limited to prevent hidden fire and smoke travel
- party walls be fire resisting.

Part B4

B4 is concerned with the prevention of fire spread from one building to another. It requires that external walls provide adequate fire resistance and that roofs should be adequately resistant to spread of flame.

A single publication produced by the Department of the Environment describes, in technical detail, the way in which the performance requirements of B2/3/4 may be satisfied. This publication, *Approved Document B*, defines, for example, periods of fire resistance according to the size and use of the building and makes reference to various British Standard tests.

The technical detail in *Approved Document B* is, in effect, equivalent to the requirements contained in the Building Regulations before their revision in 1985. However, the designer is not obliged to adopt the solution described in the Approved Document, only to satisfy the functional requirements of the Regulations. The designer may develop a different solution, or wish to convince the building control officer that, in the circumstances, the "conventional" solution in the Approved Document is unreasonable. Nevertheless, compliance with Approved Document B would tend to satisfy the Regulations. Equally, if an alternative approach is followed, it may be necessary to demonstrate that the performance requirement is still satisfied.

The performance requirement does, of course, relate only to health and safety, and not to protection of property. It is often argued that, for example, the relatively long periods of fire resistance advocated in Approved Document B for some applications are difficult to justify on the grounds of health and safety. It is, therefore, likely that some of the present guidance in the Approved Document may be relaxed in severity as an outcome of the current review.

Once a building is erected, ongoing control of fire safety is, in the case of many buildings, effected under powers granted by the Fire Precautions Act 1971 (see below). However, the Regulations control "material alterations" to a building, ie any alteration that would adversely affect the fire safety of the existing building as controlled by Parts B1, B3 or B4. Thus if, for example, part of a fire resisting enclosure, required by the Building Regulations at the time of construction, were completely removed by an occupier as part of an alteration, the occupier would be guilty of an offence, unless the alteration had been approved by the local authority.

Fire Precautions Act 1971

The Fire Precautions Act applies to offices, shops, railway premises, factories, hotels and boarding houses. In all but the smallest of these premises, a fire certificate, confirming conformity with the requirements of the Act, is required. The Act does, however, empower the fire authority to take action if persons are at serious risk from fire in a very wide range of occupancies for which a fire certificate is not required.

Designating orders

The Fire Precautions Act enables the Secretary of State at the Home Office to designate, from a wide ranging list of occupancies set out in s1 of the Act, those occupancies to which the Act applies. Designating orders have been issued for the following occupancies:

(a) hotels and boarding houses with sleeping facilities for more than six occupants, including staff as well as guests
(b) hotels and boarding houses with any sleeping facilities, whether for guests or staff, on any floor other than the ground and first floors
(c) offices, shops and railway premises, as defined in the Offices, Shops and Railways Premises Act 1963
(d) factories as defined in the Factories Act 1961.

In the case of hotels, a certification process applies to all premises within the scope of the designating order. In the case of offices, shops, railway premises and factories, the certification process applies only if there are:

(a) more than 20 persons employed or,
(b) more than 10 persons on a floor other than the ground floor.

Nevertheless, s9A of the Fire Precautions Act still requires that certain fire precautions be provided in offices, shops, railway premises and factories in which less than these numbers are employed. Also, in the case of factories in which significant quantities of explosive or highly flammable liquids are stored or used, the certification process applies regardless of the number of persons employed.

Enforcing Authorities

The Act only applies to existing premises, as opposed to new building work, which is within the scope of the Building Regulations. However, to avoid conflict between the two, or between the requirements of the relevant enforcing authorities, s13 of the Fire Precautions Act generally prohibits the authority enforcing the Fire Precautions Act from demanding means of escape requirements beyond those already required under the Building Regulations. This is known as the "statutory bar". Normally, if a certificate is required, an application must be made to the fire authority.

However, in the case of Crown Premises, application must be made to the Fire Service Inspectorate of the Home Office (in Scotland, the Scottish Home and Health Department).

Certification process

In the case of those premises for which a fire certificate is required (see above), the initial requirement of the Act is that an application for a certificate be made, or an offence is committed. However, no offence is committed by occupying and using the premises without a fire certificate, provided an application has been made. Indeed, the workload of some fire authorities, particularly in urban areas, is such that it may be many months, or even some years, before the fire authority actually responds to an application for a certificate for low risk premises, such as offices. The responsibility for the application for a certificate normally rests with the occupier. In the case of premises in multiple occupation, however, the responsibility is that of the owner of the premises.

Having applied for a certificate, the Fire Precautions Act imposes only three "interim duties" on the owner or occupier, pending disposal of the application by the enforcing authority. These duties are as follows:

(a) existing means of escape (whether adequate or not) must be maintained
(b) existing fire extinguishing appliances (whether adequate or not) must be maintained
(c) all employees must receive instruction or training in what to do in the event of fire.

This does not imply that, during the period between the application and its disposal by the enforcing authority, an occupier may ignore fire safety. General duties regarding the safety of employees continue to be imposed by the Health and Safety at Work, etc Act 1974. When the enforcing authority deal with an application for a certificate, they carry out a thorough inspection of the premises. Following the inspection, they may then follow any one of three courses of action:

(a) issue a fire certificate

(b) issue a "Notice of Steps to be Taken", requiring improvements to the fire precautions
(c) make the premises exempt from the need for a fire certificate.

Conditions of Certification

The Act only empowers the enforcing authority to issue a certificate if four matters are satisfactory. These may be summarised as follows:

1. The means of escape from fire.
2. The "supporting provisions" for the means of escape (eg, emergency lighting, signs, etc).
3. The means of raising the alarm (normally an electrical fire alarm system).
4. The means for fighting fire (ie, fire extinguishers and/or hose reels).

The Act does not empower the enforcing authority to require as a condition of certification, any fire protection measures beyond those specified above. For example, there are no powers to require sprinkler protection. Nevertheless, one clause of the Fire Safety and Safety of Places of Sport Act 1987 amends the Fire Precautions Act to enable automatic extinguishing installations to be required. This clause has not, however, been brought into effect at the time of writing, although it is likely that it will be in the foreseeable future. Thereafter, it is possible that, in the future, sprinkler protection may be required to satisfy the Fire Precautions Act in certain situations, such as complex buildings with special evacuation problems, eg enclosed shopping malls. It is not unknown for a fire authority to impose requirements for smoke ventilation as a condition of certification on the basis that it is a supporting provision for means of escape. However, in buildings such as single storey warehouses, this is of very dubious legality.

The Fire Certificate

A fire certificate does not resemble, for example an employers' liability certificate (which must be displayed prominently) although a fire certificate must be kept in the premises to which it relates. The certificate is, in fact, a complex legal document that specifies, partly by means of text but mainly by means of a set of plans, the detail of the four required fire protection measures, as existing at the time of inspection, ie:

- escape routes,
- areas that must be enclosed in fire resisting construction
- the locations of equipment, such as fire extinguishers, hose reels, fire alarm call points
- fire safety signs.

Since such detail was taken into account in certification of the premises, it must remain in being unless changes are permitted after consultation with the enforcing authority.

Section 8 of the Act requires that if, while a fire certificate is in force:

(a) it is proposed to make a *material* extension, or *material* substantial alteration, to the premises, or
(b) it is proposed to make a *material* alteration to the internal arrangements of the premises or in the furniture or equipment with which the premises are provided,

notice of the proposals must be given to the fire authority before beginning the work. (The same requirement applies if it is intended to begin to keep explosives or highly flammable materials in excess of specified limits.) If the work is started without such notice having been given, an offence is committed.

It is an offence, therefore, to alter materially the means of escape without first seeking the permission of the enforcing authority. "Materially" is not defined in the Act but is generally considered to mean make worse. It is wise to consult the enforcing authority before implementing any real changes to the measures specified in the certificate.

The certificate also normally imposes numerous general requirements on the occupier or owner of the building, as well as certain specific requirements, such as:

- managerial duties, eg regular testing and maintenance of fire equipment
- regular fire drills
- instruction of occupants in fire matters

- — the keeping of records.
- — a limit on the number of persons who may occupy the premises at any one time, etc.

It is very important that the owner or occupier carefully reads the certificate, as an offence is committed if its requirements are contravened.

Notice of steps to be taken

Following an inspection, if the enforcing authority are not satisfied regarding fire precautions in premises to which certification applies, they will issue a formal notice setting out the improvements that are considered necessary and the time within which each requirement must be implemented. The person on whom the notice is served then has 21 days in which to appeal to the magistrates court if aggrieved by the requirements imposed. Otherwise, if the requirements are not implemented within the timescale imposed (and the enforcing authority do not grant an extension to the time limit) the certificate is deemed to be refused. It is, from that time, illegal to put the premises to the designated use.

Published guidance for hotels, offices, shops, etc on the standards that should be imposed by the enforcing authority as a condition of certification, is available from HMSO. These guides contain a great deal of technical detail, particularly in respect of means of escape. They also make reference to relevant British Standards, which give technical guidance concerning emergency lighting installations, fire alarm installations, hose reel installations, fire extinguisher provision, etc. Although intended for enforcing authorities, these guides are extremely useful for architects, consultants and others who may wish to anticipate the requirements of the enforcing authorities.

Exemptions

An enforcing authority can exempt from the certification process, certain smaller premises in which the risk to occupants is low. Exemptions only apply to offices, shops, railway premises and factories. In the case of shops, exemptions may be granted only if the shop is located on a ground floor, or on the ground floor and basement of a building in which the basement is separated from the ground floor by fire resisting construction. In the case of offices, railway premises and factories, exemptions may be granted to premises that are located on:

(a) a ground floor
(b) a ground floor and first floor
(c) a ground floor and basement
(d) a ground floor, first floor and basement of a building in which the basement is separated from the ground floor by fire resisting construction.

In determining whether or not premises are suitable for exemption, the enforcing authority will take into account the nature of the fire risk to occupants. In exempting the premises from certification, the enforcing authority may impose a limit on the number of occupants. An exemption may be withdrawn at any time if the risk changes. The granting of exemptions is entirely the prerogative of the enforcing authority with no right of appeal.

Premises for which an exemption is granted are treated in the same manner as those to which the certification process does not apply. A flowchart summarising the fire certification process appears in Table 1.

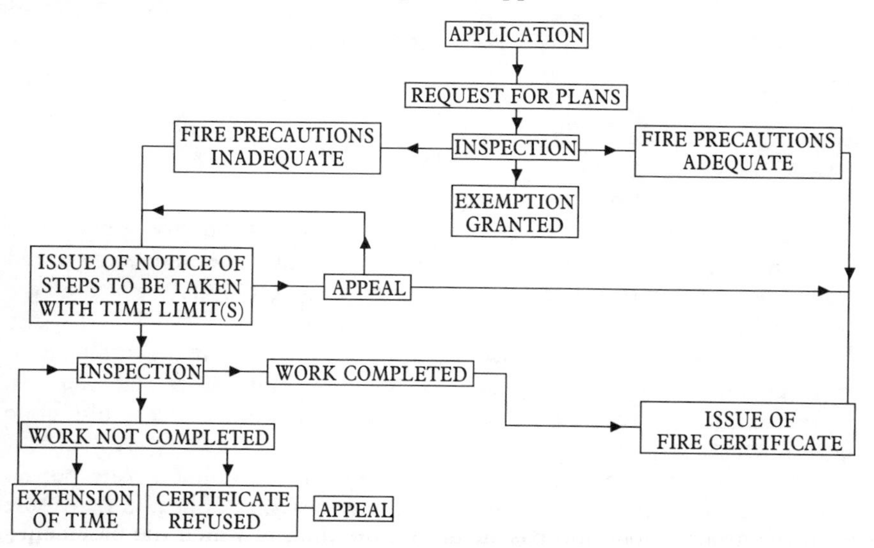

Table 1: Fire certification process

Non-certificated premises

Offices, shops, railway premises and factories for which a fire certificate is not required (either by virtue of the number of persons employed or by virtue of an exemption) are required by s9A of the Fire Precautions Act to have adequate means of escape and adequate means for fighting fire. Such premises are, therefore, not specifically required by law to have a fire alarm system. In practice, however, the safety of occupants might be enhanced, or even depend upon, the presence of a fire alarm system.

The responsibility for ensuring that the requirements of s9A are satisfied, rests with the occupier (or, in the case of a building in multiple occupation, the owner). Guidance on the technical requirements for both means of escape and firefighting equipment is contained in a code of practice produced by the Home Office and published by HMSO. This code has no statutory force but compliance would tend to demonstrate that the requirements of legislation have been satisfied.

Failure to comply with s9A is an offence. If the enforcing authority do not consider that premises comply with the requirements of s9A, they may issue an improvement notice specifying the work required for compliance. The person on whom the notice is served then has the right of appeal to the Court, provided this is lodged within 21 days of receipt of the notice.

Prohibition notices

If the fire authority are of the opinion that use of premises involves a very serious risk to occupants in the event of fire, they are empowered to serve a prohibition notice, which restricts or prohibits the use of the premises. This power applies to any of the premises listed in s1 of the Fire Precautions Act, which includes any used for sleeping accommodation (except private dwellings), hospitals, schools, universities, laboratories, entertainment or recreational establishments and other places of public assembly.

In practice, the use of this power is relatively uncommon. Any person on whom a prohibition notice is served, however, may appeal to the Court within 21 days. The lodging of an appeal does not suspend the notice unless the Court so directs.

Offices Shops and Railway Premises Act 1963 and Factories Act 1961 Certificates

"Means of escape certificates" were no longer issued under these Acts after 1976, when offices, shops, railway premises and factories were designated under the Fire Precautions Act. However, existing certificates are deemed to be Fire Precautions Act certificates, (and therefore satisfy the Fire Precautions Act), until material changes take place and a new certificate has to be produced.

The means of escape certificates did not, however, impose all the requirements now imposed by the Fire Precautions Act certificates. A complicated situation now arises whereby, if reliance is placed on a means of escape certificate (issued under the 1961 and 1963 Acts) to satisfy the requirement for a Fire Precautions Act certificate, various repealed sections of these Acts are also deemed to apply. The sections in question are set out in schedule 8 to the Health and Safety at Work, etc Act 1974. However, there remain certain differences between the requirements imposed by the means of escape certificate (plus the relevant sections of the associated Acts) and those arising from a modern Fire Precautions Act certificate. Nevertheless, as already indicated, the means of escape certificate will be withdrawn and a Fire Precautions Act certificate issued, (imposing a wide range of requirements and duties), when material changes occur and the original certificate is no longer appropriate.

The Fire Certificates (Special Premises) Regulations 1976

These Regulations apply to industrial premises in which there is a high risk of fire or explosion because of highly flammable materials or dangerous chemicals. In these situations fire certificates are issued by the Health and Safety Executive (HSE) rather than by the fire authority. The types of fire precautions covered by the certificate are the same as those covered by a certificate issued under the Fire Precautions Act 1971, ie means of escape, fire fighting and fire warning systems. HSE Inspectors enforce these Regulations.

The fire certificate for "special premises" will cover the whole site, including access roads and open land, as well as any buildings. Persons may not work on the site unless either there is a valid certificate and its conditions are complied with, or an application for a certificate has been made.

Designated "special premises" under the 1976 Regulations

Sites where there are large quantities of specified dangerous substances come under the provisions of the Regulations. The substances and amounts are listed in the table below:

Activity	Substance	Quantity (tonnes)
Manufacturing	Pressurised highly flammable liquid	50
Manufacturing	Expanded cellular plastics	50 per week
Storage	Liquefied petroleum gas (not as fuel)	100
Storage	Liquefied natural gas (not as fuel)	100
Storage	Methyl acetylene gas (not as fuel)	100
Manufacture and storage	Liquid oxygen	135
Storage	Chlorine (not for water purification)	50
Manufacture and storage of fertilisers	Ammonia	250
Process, manufacture, use and storage	Phosgene	5
	Ethylene oxide	20
	Carbon disulphide	50
	Acrylonitrile	50
	Hydrogen cyanide	50
	Ethylene	100
	Propylene	100
	Other highly flammable liquid	4000

Other types of special premises are:

(a) licensed explosives factories and magazines
(b) surface buildings at mine sites
(c) nuclear sites
(d) sites with high voltage machinery/apparatus (not hospitals)
(e) certain sites containing highly radioactive material
(f) buildings at construction sites which are used for purposes connected with building or engineering work (unless certain conditions are met, eg less than 20 people are employed and adequate fire precautions are provided).

The Regulations also cover matters such as contents of the fire certificate, changes of conditions, appeals and exemptions.

Local Acts

It would be incorrect to assume that, in designing, building and occupying a building for a use that is designated under the Fire Precautions Act, only the national Building Regulations and the Fire Precautions Act apply. In some areas of England and Wales, local Acts impose additional requirements for certain categories of premises, such as high buildings and large storage buildings.

Perhaps the most well known local legislation is that contained in s20 of the London Building Acts (Amendment) Act 1935 (as amended by the Building (Inner London) Regulations 1985). This legislation empowers London district surveyors to require special fire safety measures, such as sprinkler protection, in certain high buildings, or large uncompartmented buildings used for manufacturing or warehousing, in inner London. Requirements of local Acts are not generally concerned with means of escape for occupants but with measures that will limit the extent of fire spread and assist the fire brigade. In Scotland, measures to assist the fire brigade are already contained in the Building Standards (Scotland) Regulations 1990. In the future, such measures will also be incorporated in the revised version of the Building Regulations that apply in England and Wales. In the meantime, Reference 7 contains an excellent review of the requirements contained in each of 31 local Acts.

Miscellaneous Legislation

Fire safety legislation remains dispersed through various statutes that give control to a number of authorities. The reader with particular interest in fire safety legislation should consult Reference 6 in the bibliography at the end of this chapter. It is not feasible to list all legislation that, to a greater or lesser extent, impinges on fire safety. However, the following legislation contains requirements of particular importance to the types of occupancy indicated in parentheses.

(a) Housing Act 1985 (houses in multiple occupation)
(b) s71 of the Building Act 1984 (certain places of assembly, such as clubs, shops and restaurants employing more than 20 persons, theatres, schools and certain churches)
(c) Cinemas Act 1985 (cinemas)
(d) Theatres Act 1968 (theatres)
(e) Licensing Act 1964 (premises licensed for the sale of alcohol)
(f) s72 of the Building Act 1984 (buildings of more than two storeys and greater than 20 feet in height used for various specified purposes that normally incorporate sleeping accommodation).

Note. Sections 71 and 72 of the Building Act do not apply to premises for which a fire certificate has been issued under the Fire Precautions Act, or premises for which Building Regulations require adequate means of escape.

Other legislation, such as the Local Government (Miscellaneous Provisions) Act 1982, enables local authorities to impose fire safety requirements as a condition of a licence for premises in which there is music, singing and dancing.

The above list is far from exhaustive and it is important to consult the appropriate authority, such as the fire authority, to determine the legislation that may be relevant in the case of any particular premises.

Civil Liability

Civil liability for loss or injury as a result of fire can arise in certain circumstances. The increasing awareness of the potential for litigation is likely to ensure that claims against occupiers or owners of property involved in fire will continue to arise. Liability to visitors to the premises, for example is established by the Occupiers Liability Acts. In a recent case, a fireman successfully sued a householder for his injuries, incurred while fighting a fire. The fire started due to the negligence of the householder while undertaking work in the premises.

With regard to fire spreading to neighbouring property, the Fire Prevention (Metropolis) Act 1774 provides that:

> No action suit or process whatsoever shall be had, maintained or prosecuted against any person in whose house, chamber, stable, barn, or other building, or on whose estate any fire shall accidentally begin.

It has, however, been shown quite clearly that if a fire starts or spreads due to negligence or the presence of dangerous substances, rather than *by accident*, then liability arises.

Summary

The following table summarises the principal legislation that applies to common industrial and commercial premises.

OCCUPANCY	PRINCIPAL LEGISLATION AFFECTING FIRE SAFETY IN NEW BUILDINGS	PRINCIPAL LEGISLATION AFFECTING FIRE SAFETY IN EXISTING BUILDINGS	CIRCUMSTANCES IN WHICH A FIRE CERTIFICATE IS REQUIRED	MAIN OTHER RELEVANT FIRE RELATED LEGISLATION
OFFICES	B1/B2/B3/B4 of Schedule 1 to the Buildings Regulations	Fire Precautions Act	(a) More than 20 persons employed to work at one time (b) More than 10 persons employed to work at one time on a floor above or below ground	In some areas of England and Wales local Acts apply to high buildings
SHOPS	B1/B2/B3/B4 of Schedule 1 to the Buildings Regulations	Fire Precautions Act	(a) More than 20 persons employed to work at one time (b) More than 10 persons employed to work at one time on a floor above or below ground	In some areas of England and Wales Local Acts apply
INDUSTRIAL BUILDINGS	B2/B3/B4 of Schedule 1 to the Building Regulations	Fire Precautions Act	(a) More than 20 persons employed to work at one time (b) More than 10 persons employed to work at one time on a floor above or below ground (c) Explosive or highly flammable materials are stored or used (other than materials of a type or quantity that do not create an additional risk)	In some areas of England and Wales Local Acts may apply
HOTELS AND BOARDING HOUSES	B2/B3/B4 of Schedule 1 to the Building Regulations	Fire Precautions Act (except in the case of hotels that do not provide sleeping accommodation for more than six persons, including guests and staff, and in which no person sleeps above first floor level or below ground floor level)	All premises other than those exempt from the Fire Precautions Act.	In some areas of England and Wales Local Acts may apply

Table 2: Summary of principal fire legislation

Further reading

1. *The Building Regulations 1985 (SI 1985/1065)*. HMSO ISBN 0 11 751815.
2. *Department of the Environment Manual to the Building Regulations 1985*. HMSO ISBN 0 117 518166.
3. Fire Precautions Act 1971 (as amended).
4. *Fire Prevention Design Guide 1: Fire and the Law*. Fire Protection Association.
5. *Fire Safety Data Sheet OR1: Fire Protection Law*. Fire Protection Association.
6. Everton A, Hollyoak J and Allen A, *Fire Safety and the Law*, 2nd Edition. Paramount Publishing Ltd. ISBN 0 947 665137.
7. Pitt, P H, *Guide to Building Control by Local Acts*. Architectural Press ISBN 0 851 398413.

Chapter 2

The Nature of Fire

Components of Fire: the Fire Triangle

In terms of basic chemistry, fire is an exothermic (heat releasing) chemical reaction between a fuel and oxygen. A very simple model of fire is often represented in the form of the "fire triangle' (see Figure 1), which shows the three components that are required in order for fire to occur:

(a) heat (in the form of an ignition source)
(b) fuel (the combustible material ignited)
(c) oxygen (which is usually present in sufficient quantities for combustion to be sustained).

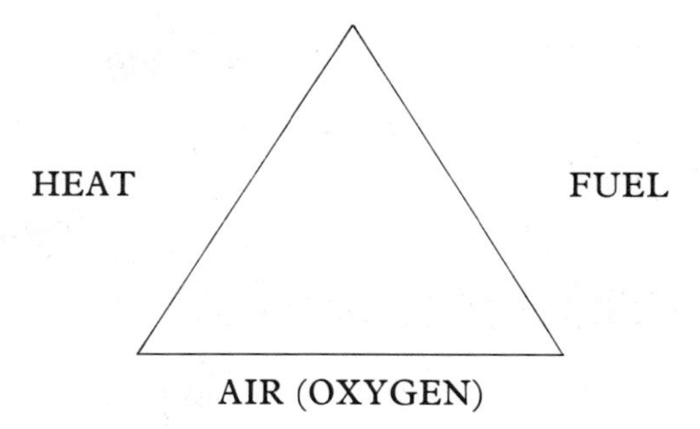

Figure 1: The fire triangle: removal of any component obviates the risk of fire

The significance of this simple model is that fire cannot occur if any one of the three components is removed. Of course, it is not normally possible to remove, or sufficiently reduce, the oxygen content of the atmosphere. Complete removal of all fuel is equally impracticable although, as discussed in Chapter 5, measures such as removal of waste, security of flammable liquids storage and the avoidance of unnecessary storage, all contribute to the prevention of fire. It is, therefore, necessary to avoid the introduction of the ever-present ignition sources to the ever-present fuel.

The Combustion of Solid Materials

Although it is not obvious from common experience, solid materials do not, in fact, "burn". Flame is actually a vapour phase chemical reaction between fuel *vapour* and oxygen. For example, when a source of heat is applied to a piece of wood (see Figure 2), the chemical constituents of the wood (mainly cellulose) begin to break down, releasing vapours that comprise a complex mixture of flammable compounds. It is these vapours that then ignite to form a flame. The combustion of the vapours in the

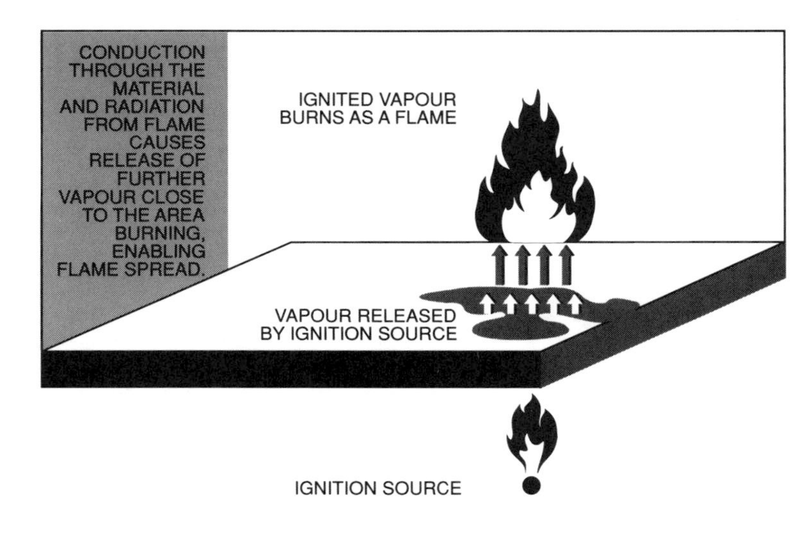

Figure 2: Combustion of a solid

presence of oxygen releases heat, a significant proportion of which is transferred to the surface of the wood, so releasing more vapours to enter what is now a closed feedback loop (see Figure 3). The source of heat

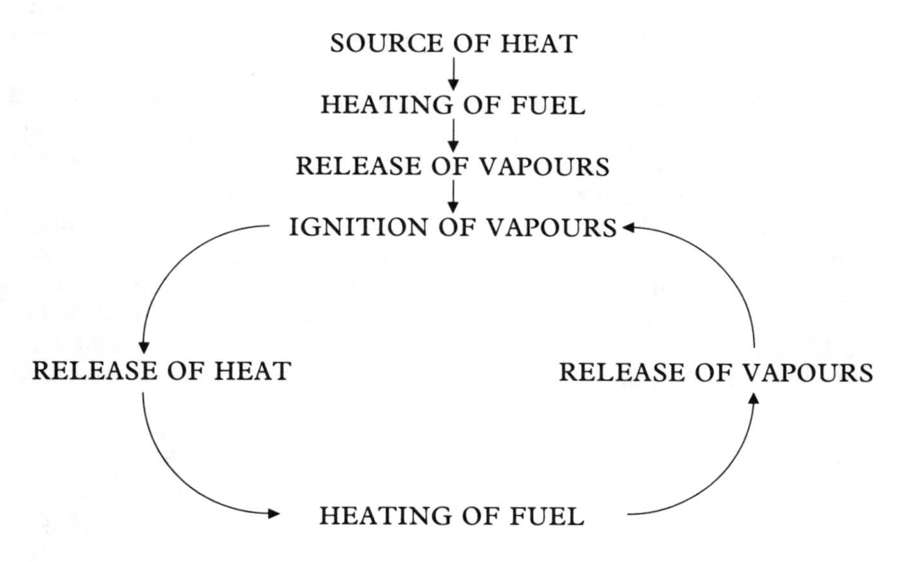

Figure 3: The feedback loop of fire

shown in Figure 3 is usually an external ignition source, but it should be noted in passing that some materials can "self heat" resulting in "spontaneous combustion". A simple example is the case of a heap of oil soaked rags in a warm cupboard. An understanding of Figures 2 and 3 also leads to an explanation of the reason why solid materials burn more readily if they are sub-divided into a finer form. A thin fuel (eg a sheet of paper) ignites more readily and burns more fiercely than a thick fuel (eg a book) because the heat sink effect is less.

The Combustion of Flammable Liquids

It is not the liquid that burns, but the vapour above the liquid surface. Some liquids, such as castor oil and olive oil, behave in a similar manner to solids in that they require the application of a substantial amount of heat before they will ignite. Such liquids are generally considered to be combustible. Other liquids, such as white spirit and paraffin, require much less heat in order to release sufficient vapour for ignition to occur. These liquids can be considered to be flammable and pose a greater hazard. Yet other liquids, such as petrol and ether, produce sufficient vapour, even below normal room temperature, to enable ignition of the vapour/air mixture by a small ignition source, such as a spark. Clearly, these liquids are particularly hazardous and require special precautions to ensure that the vapour is not permitted to come into contact with a source of igntion.

A useful measure of the hazard of any flammable liquid is its "flashpoint". This is the minimum temperature at which, in a specific test, the liquid gives off sufficient vapour to ignite on application of the ignition source specified in the test. Obviously, the higher the flashpoint of a liquid, the less hazardous it is. The flashpoint of many vegetable oils, for example, exceeds 200°C. At the other extreme, the flashpoint of petrol is, typically, -43°C.

The flashpoint of a flammable liquid, such as a solvent, will generally be marked on the container. Generally, a liquid is considered to be flammable if its flashpoint is between 32°C and 55°C. Liquids with flashpoints below 32°C are defined as highly flammable; the storage and use of such liquids in premises to which the Factories Act 1961 applies, is governed by the Highly Flammable Liquids and Liquefied Petroleum Gases Regulations 1972. (These Regulations do not, however, cover petroleum mixtures with a flashpoint of less than 23°C, to which the Petroleum (Consolidation) Act 1928 applies.) The Regulations deal with matters such as method of storage, ventilation, and limitation of quantities introduced to the workplace.

Other, more subsidiary, measures of the hazard posed by a flammable liquid include the flammability limits of the vapour and the auto-ignition temperature. The flammability limits are the proportions (expressed as a percentage) in which the flammable vapour must be present in air, for an explosion to occur on ignition of the vapour. Outside these limits, the vapour/air mixture is either too weak or too rich to ignite. Obviously, wide flammability limits constitute a greater hazard than very narrow limits. A knowledge of the limits can be useful in determining the necessary amount of ventilation and the maximum acceptable concentration of vapour.

Auto-ignition temperature is, perhaps, of less significance. It is the temperature at which the liquid will ignite without the presence of an actual ignition source (such as occurs when a pan of cooking oil is left unattended on a source of heat). Normally, auto-ignition temperatures of flammable and highly flammable liquids are quite high (eg 200–600°C).

However, some liquids, notably vegetable and fish oils, when absorbed onto rags, etc may be subject to spontaneous heating and ultimately ignition, despite the fact that flashpoints and auto-ignition temperatures may be very high.

The Combustion of Flammable Gases

In practice, there is little distinction between the combustion of flammable vapours arising from substances that are liquids at normal temperatures and pressure, and the combustion of flammable substances that are gaseous at normal temperature and pressure. In the case of gases, of course, the question of flashpoint does not arise, and an indication of the hazard may be given by the flammability limits. As in the case of flammable liquids, auto-ignition temperature is of less significance and, again, tends to range between 200°C and 600°C for most common flammable gases.

In most commercial, and many industrial premises, the presence of flammable gases, other than those used as a fuel for heating and cooking, will be uncommon. A possible exception arises during contractors' operations, when some activities such as cutting and welding may involve the use of acetylene or liquefied petroleum gas (LPG), the latter of which may also be used for temporary heating or as a fuel for tar boilers, etc. The main hazard associated with acetylene is the very wide explosive limits of the gas. The explosive limits of LPG are much narrower, but a particular hazard is its density, which is greater than that of air. The gas can, therefore, collect in low lying areas, such as basements, pits and drains.

The Mechanism of Extinguishment

In order to extinguish a fire, it is necessary to break the feedback loop shown in Figures 2 and 3. Thus, water (the most common extinguishing agent) extinguishes a fire primarily by cooling the fuel, so that it no longer releases sufficient vapour to enable combustion to be sustained. Foam applied to, for example, the surface of a burning liquid, acts as a physical barrier, which prevents the release of vapour into the combustion zone above the surface of the liquid. More importantly, the barrier also reduces the effect of radiation from the flame onto the fuel surface. In addition, drainage of water from the foam may assist in cooling the hot liquid.

The action of carbon dioxide is straightforward. It displaces oxygen to a sufficient extent to stop the combustion process. Thus, it directly removes one of the three components of the fire triangle.

The mechanism by which halons extinguish fire is more complex. The effect of halon is to interfere with the chemical reactions that occur within flames. The so-called "chemical inhibition" of flame is a subject outside the scope of this book but a detailed explanation is given in Reference 7. The point to note at this stage is that chemical inhibition is very much more effective than straightforward oxygen displacement, and the concentration of halon required to extinguish a fire is significantly less than the concentration of carbon dioxide.

The means by which dry powders extinguish fires is not fully understood. However, it is probable that chemical inhibition is a major factor, as well as dilution of the fuel vapour and removal of heat. Whatever the exact mechanism, the effect of dry powder, like that of the halons, is rapid knockdown of flame.

Classification of Fires

In order to consider the suitability of different extinguishing agents for different types of fire (see Chapter 11), fires are grouped into classes, according to the nature of the fuel. In the United Kingdom, the classification system used is defined in British Standard 4547, which is a harmonised European standard. The classification system is as follows:

Class A fires are those involving "normal" (usually carbonaceous) solid materials, such as wood, textiles and paper, which form glowing embers when they burn.
Class B fires are those involving liquids or liquefiable solids.
Class C fires involve gases.
Class D fires involve metals.

Class C and D fires are not of major practical significance in most premises. In the case of Class C fires, the use of a fire extinguisher may be very undesirable since these fires often arise from a continuous leak of gas from, for example, a cylinder. Extinguishment of the burning gas may result in an explosion if no action is taken to prevent the leak from continuing. Class D fires require special extinguishing agents.

The Development and Spread of Fire

Once ignition of a fire in an enclosure has occurred, the subsequent development may be rapid. Mathematically, the development is often described as exponential; in simple terms, fire tends to double in size at regular intervals of perhaps only a matter of a few minutes. This rapidity of growth is beyond the common experience of most building occupants, as it contrasts sharply with the more commonly experienced, sedate behaviour of a fire in the open (eg a garden bonfire). This inability to anticipate the rate of development of a fire in a building has proved to be a major factor in certain multiple fatality fires involving members of the public, who failed to appreciate the need for immediate evacuation and died as a result. Examples include the fires at Woolworths, Manchester in 1979, the Stardust discotheque, Dublin in 1981 and the Bradford football stadium in 1985.

Fire develops by heat transfer, ie conduction, convection and radiation. The most important means of fire spread within a building are, however, convection and radiation.

After the first item in the enclosure is ignited, hot gases rise vertically in a relatively narrow plume, into which air is entrained, so increasing the volume of the smoke and gases. As the smoke reaches the ceiling it spreads out in all directions and, ultimately, begins to form a rapidly deepening layer below the ceiling (see Figure 4). Thus, particularly in the case of a restricted space, such as a corridor, loss of visibility may be one of the earliest threats created by the fire.

As the fire grows, the flames reach the ceiling and are deflected horizontally, radiating downwards over a large area of the enclosure (see Figure 5). The radiation is so strong that flame will spread rapidly over combustible surfaces, and items over a relatively large area will reach a temperature at which they spontaneously burst into flames. In the case of a restricted enclosure, such as a cellular office, this stage, known as "flashover", may be reached quite quickly. At flashover, virtually all items in the room are alight, and survival of occupants within the room is impossible.

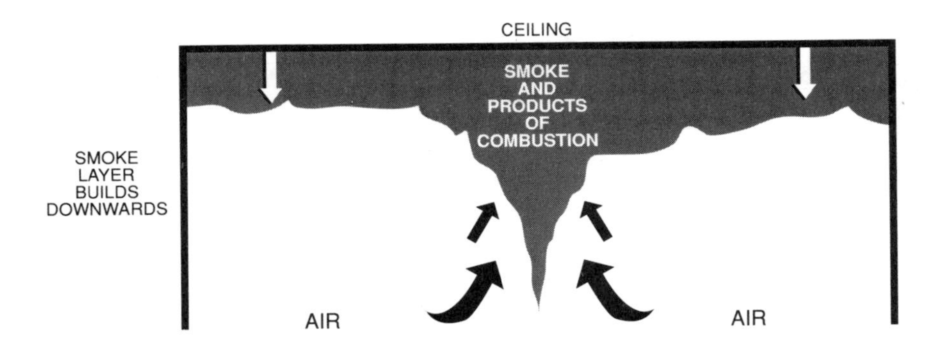

Figure 4: The build up of the smoke layer

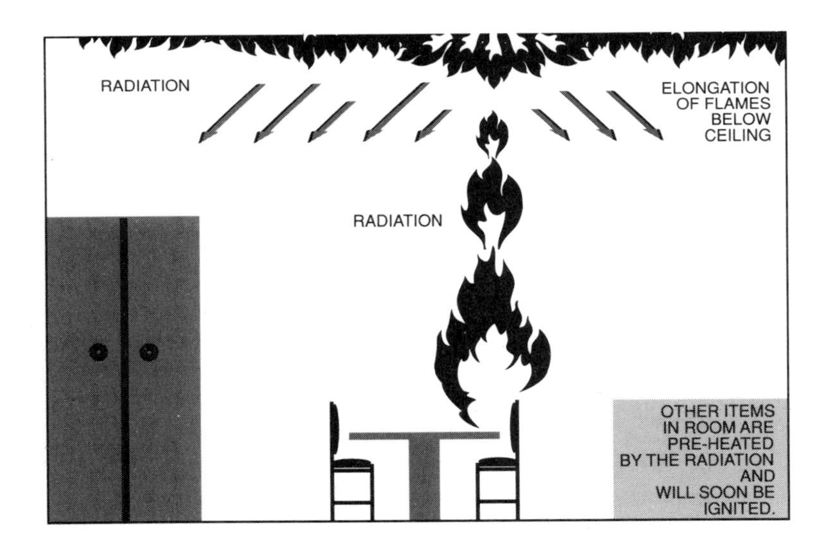

Figure 5: The onset of flashover

The progress of a fire in a building can be divided into three distinct phases (see Figure 6):

(a) a growth period, during which the average temperature in the room of origin rises relatively slowly
(b) a post-flashover period, during which the temperature is very high (owing to the involvement of most combustible items in the enclosure)
(c) a decay period that arises from the total consumption of most of the combustible materials, and continues until there remains no fuel for combustion.

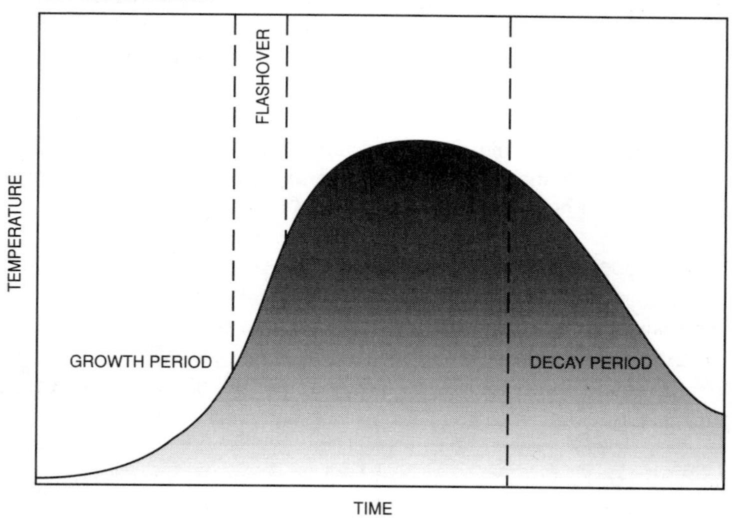

Figure 6: Simple model of a fire in an enclosure
(*after Introduction to Fire Dynamics,* DD Drysdale. John Wiley & Sons. 0 471 90613 1)

Escape from the compartment involved must be made well before flashover. There must, therefore, be adequate measures to ensure that rapid escape from a building is possible (see Chapter 6). During the post-flashover phase, the structure of the compartment is put under stress and structural fire precautions assume a greater significance (see Chapter 7). Before the building structure is seriously threatened, however, fire and smoke spread is often assisted by open doors, poorly stopped service penetrations and structural features such as service shafts and risers which, unless very effectively fire stopped, will enable the spread of smoke, and perhaps fire, from one floor to another by convection.

Fire Resistance

The most fundamental means of protecting escape routes and preventing fire spread comprises *fire resisting construction*. The meaning of this term is rather self evident, although the exact definition of the term *fire resisting* is not always well understood. Fire resistance is defined in British Standard 4422 Part 2 as the:

> ability of an element of building construction, component or structure to fulfil, for a stated period of time, the required stability, fire integrity and/or thermal insulation and/or other expected duty in a standard fire resistance test.

Three points emerge from the definition.

(a) fire resistance can only be defined in terms of a standard test
(b) the units of fire resistance are units of time
(c) fire resistance may relate to any one or all of three performance parameters.

In the United Kingdom, the standard test for fire resistance is that described in British Standard 476 Part 20. In this test, construction such as walls, floors, ceilings, doorsets and glazing systems are subjected to the heat from a furnace in accordance with a time/temperature curve that is contained in the British Standard (see Figure 7). The curve is intended to simulate the temperature/time profile experienced in a post-flashover fire.

Detailed test requirements for loadbearing elements of construction, including the criteria for pass or failure of the test, are set out in BS 476 Part 21. In the case of non-loadbearing elements of construction, the requirements are described in BS 476 Part 22. Loadbearing elements of construction may be tested for the three performance parameters defined in BS 4422, namely:

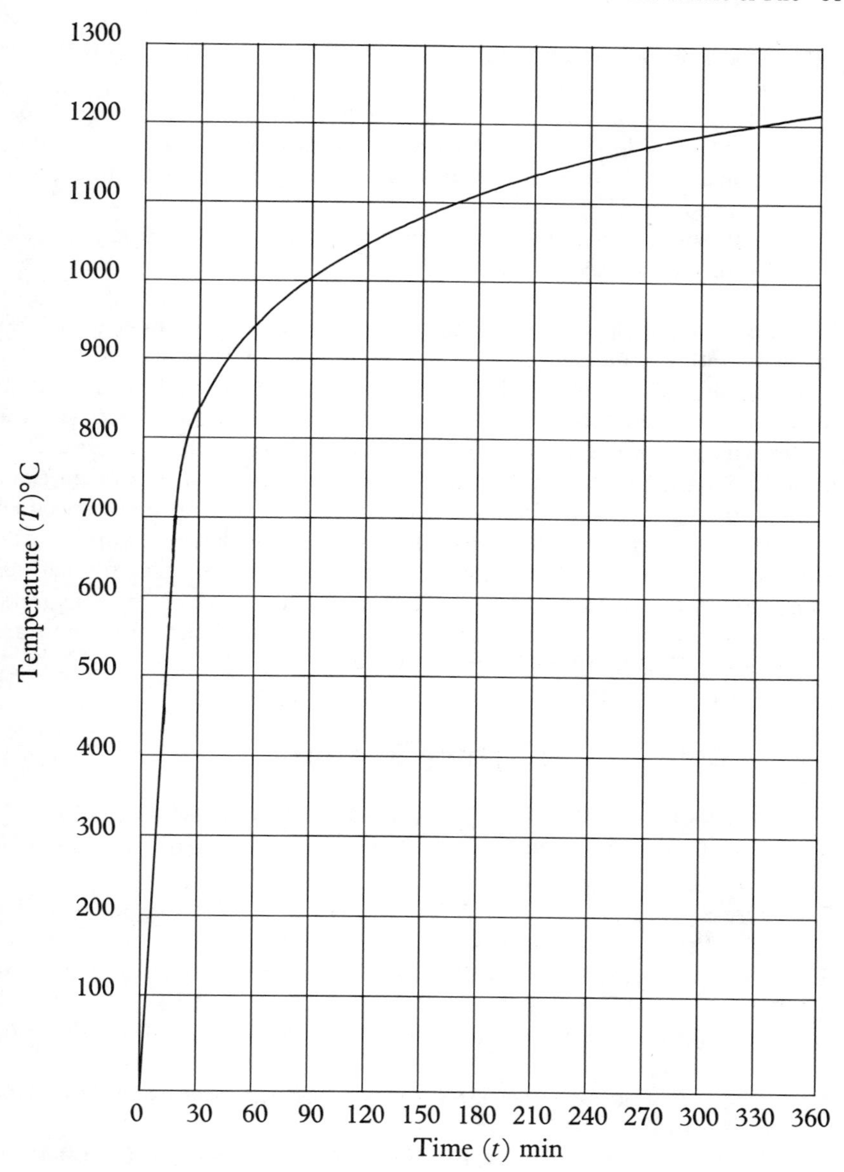

Figure 7: Time temperature curve of BS 476 Part 20

(a) loadbearing capacity, ie the ability of the element to support its test load without excessive deformation
(b) integrity, ie the ability of the element to contain a fire without collapse or the development of holes or cracks through which flame could easily pass, and without sustained flaming on the side unexposed to the furnace
(c) insulation, ie the ability of the element to resist the passage of heat from the exposed to the unexposed face.

Non-loadbearing elements of construction are, of course, only tested for integrity and insulation.

The results of these tests only indicate the performance of the construction in units of time. Other standards and regulations then indicate the performance required for elements of construction, such as doorsets, etc according to the application. In practice, with the exception of cross-corridor smoke stop doors, the minimum period of fire resistance normally specified is 30 minutes; this is regarded as a norm for protection of escape routes. However, longer periods of fire resistance may be specified for various elements of construction, either in Building Regulations or by fire insurers. Requirements for means of escape and for structural fire protection are discussed in Chapters 6 and 7 respectively.

Further Reading

1. *Fire Safety Booklet 3: What is Fire?* Fire Protection Association.
2. *Fire Safety Data Sheet NB1: Physics and Chemistry of Fire.* Fire Protection Association.
3. *Fire Safety Data Sheet NB2: Ignition, Growth and Development of Fire.* Fire Protection Association.
4. *Fire Safety Data Sheet NB3: The Physiological Effects of Fire.* Fire Protection Association.
5. *Fire Safety Data Sheet NB4: The Combustion Process.* Fire Protection Association.
6. *Fire Safety Data Sheet NB5: Auto Ignition Temperature.* Fire Protection Association.
7. Wharry DM and Hirst R, *Fire Technology, Chemistry and Combustion.* The Institution of Fire Engineers.

Chapter 3

The Causes of Fire

Many fires are the result of human failings, such as carelessness, malicious intent or simple incompetence in management. Even in the case of a fire started by faulty electrical wiring, greater attention to maintenance and safety might have prevented an incident occurring. This rather philosophical approach does little, however, to reduce the incidence of fire; it is necessary to analyse statistics concerning sources of ignition in order to obtain information on which fire prevention may be based.

There are useful sources of such information:

(a) United Kingdom fire statistics, which are published annually by the Home Office
(b) "large fire" analyses, which are produced by the Fire Protection Association (FPA), part of the Loss Prevention Council (LPC).

The United Kingdom fire statistics are based on reports that fire brigades complete each time they attend a fire. The statistics can only be as accurate as the opinion of the officer in charge at each fire. Nevertheless, the statistics provide very useful information on fire risk. The LPC is funded by fire insurers, and the "large fire" analyses are based primarily on information provided by the insurers concerning fires that result in a financial loss that exceeds a certain value—currently £50,000.

Figure 8 is based on the United Kingdom fire statistics for the year 1989. In practice, although there are noticeable trends over a number of years, the relative prevalence of each of the ignition sources defined does not vary greatly between one year and another. The statistics shown relate to all fires attended by fire brigades in the United Kingdom.

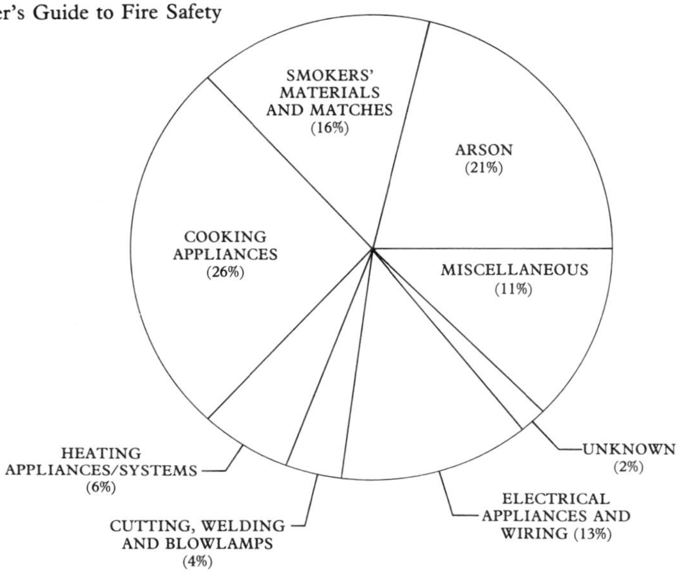

Figure 8: Causes of fire in the UK

The most significant points to emerge from the statistics are that:

(a) most fires result from a very small number of causes
(b) more specifically, 50 per cent of all fires are the result of either arson, careless use or disposal of cigarettes and matches (including fires caused by children playing with matches), or electrical sources of ignition (including fires caused by electrical appliances and wiring).

The importance of these three sources of ignition in industrial and commercial premises is reinforced if fires in dwellings are removed from the statistics since, in the latter case, the largest single source of ignition is cooking appliances. Figure 9 shows the sources of ignition of fires in non-domestic premises during 1989.

The causes of fire vary from one type of occupancy to another. This is demonstrated by Figures 10–16, which respectively show the 1989 statistics on causes of fire in industrial premises, hotels and similar premises, schools and other educational establishments, places of public entertainment and similar premises, retail premises, hospitals, and restaurants, cafes and public houses.

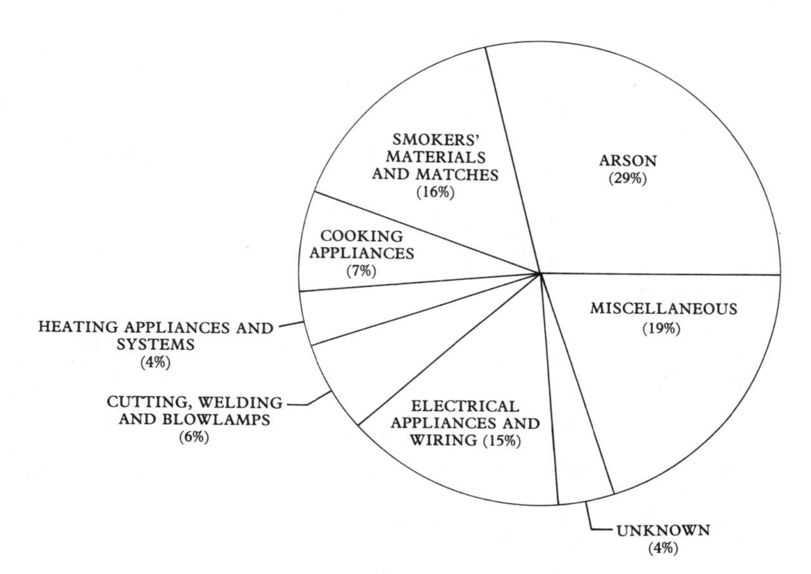

Figure 9: Causes of fire in non-domestic premises

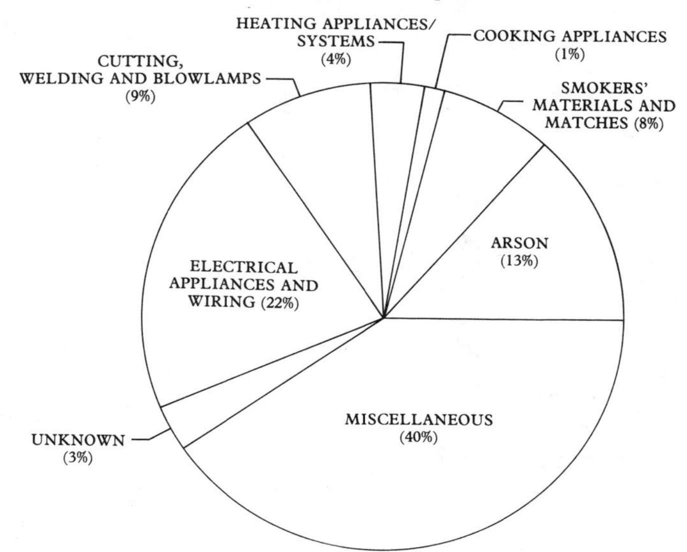

Figure 10: Causes of fire in industrial premises

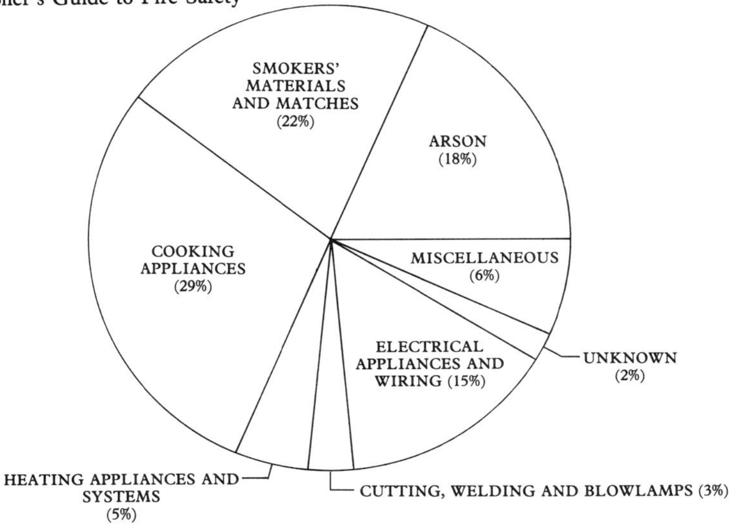

SMOKERS' MATERIALS AND MATCHES (22%)
ARSON (18%)
COOKING APPLIANCES (29%)
MISCELLANEOUS (6%)
ELECTRICAL APPLIANCES AND WIRING (15%)
UNKNOWN (2%)
HEATING APPLIANCES AND SYSTEMS (5%)
CUTTING, WELDING AND BLOWLAMPS (3%)

Figure 11: Causes of fire in hotels, hostels and boarding houses

ARSON (49%)
SMOKERS' MATERIALS AND MATCHES (11%)
MISCELLANEOUS (11%)
COOKING APPLIANCES (5%)
UNKNOWN (3%)
HEATING APPLIANCES AND SYSTEMS (4%)
CUTTING, WELDING AND BLOWLAMPS (5%)
ELECTRICAL APPLIANCES AND WIRING (12%)

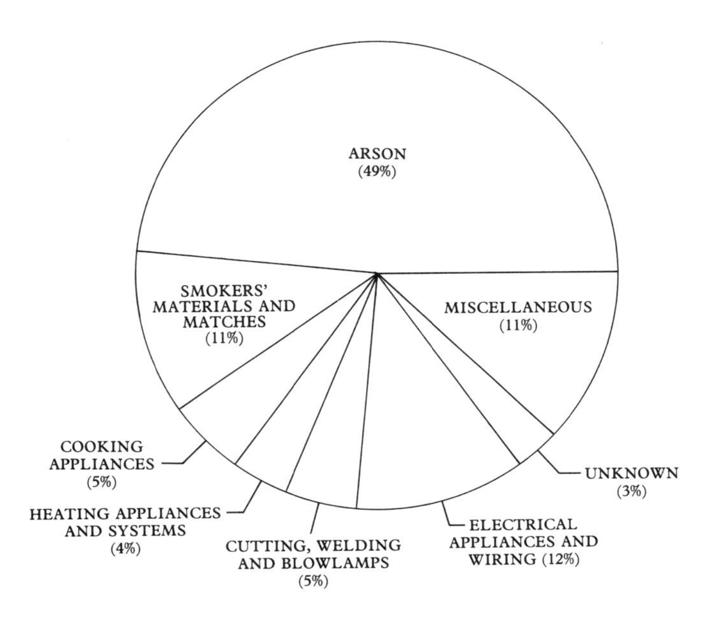

Figure 12: Causes of fire in educational establishments

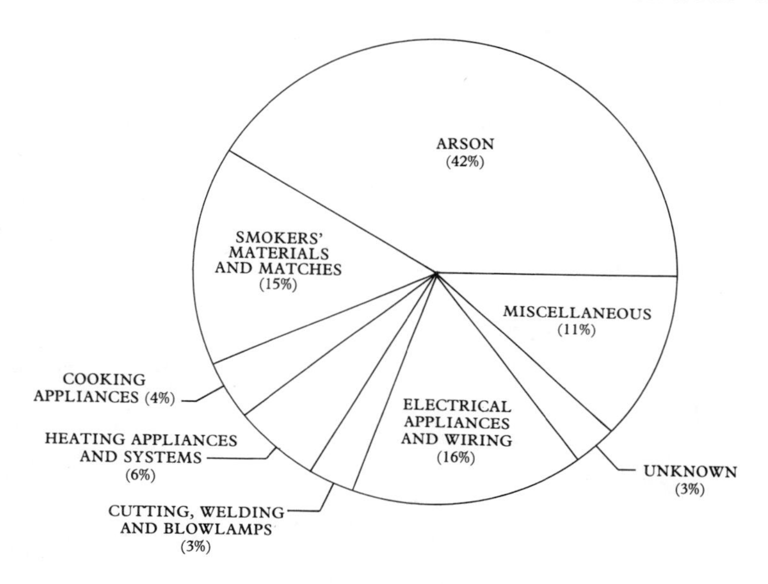

Figure 13: Causes of fire in recreational and cultural premises

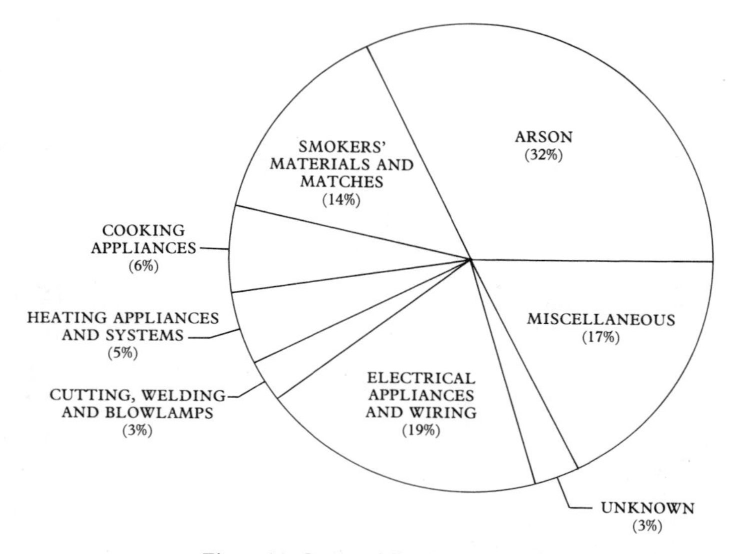

Figure 14: Causes of fire in retail premises

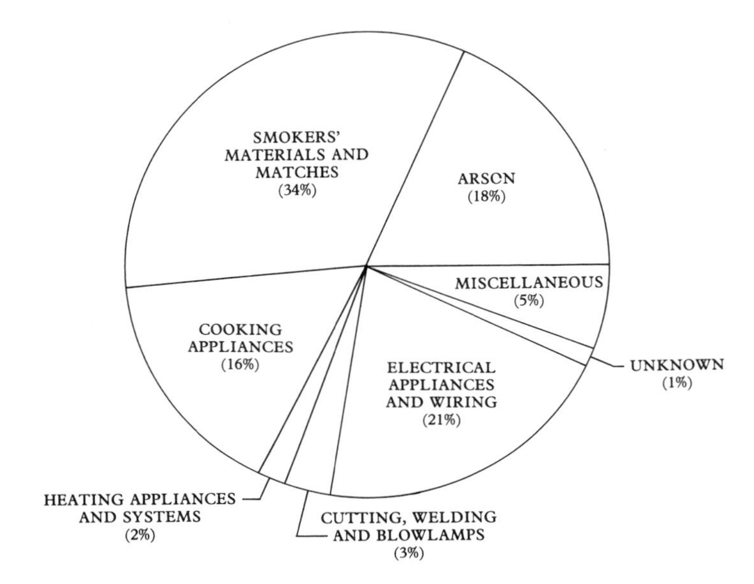

Figure 15: Causes of fire in hospitals

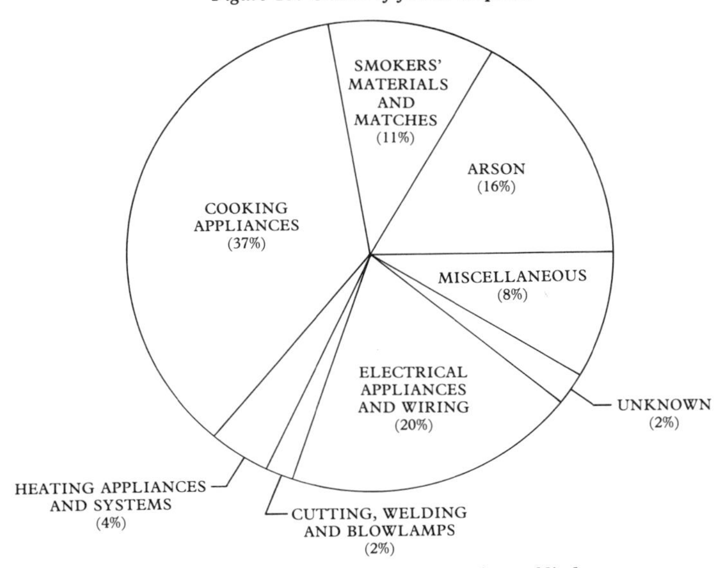

Figure 16: Causes of fire in restaurants, cafes, public houses, etc

A number of points emerge from a study of these figures:

(a) Arson is the most common single cause of fire in non-domestic premises. Some types of premises, such as schools, are particularly prone to arson. Moreover, arson is an important cause of fire in most of the premises to which members of the public are admitted. Arson is probably less common in industrial premises owing to stricter control over access.
(b) Cutting, welding and blowlamps are a small, but very significant, source of ignition. This highlights the significance of contractors' operations as a cause of fire.
(c) In hotels and restaurants, a significant number of fires involve cooking processes but, as a source of ignition, cooking appliances are less significant in other occupancies.
(d) In industry, there is a large number of miscellaneous causes, often associated with the processes undertaken. The causes of fire therefore tend to be more diverse than fires in commercial establishments.
(e) Heating appliances and installations cause only a small but consistent proportion of fires. Of these fires, space heating appliances account for the majority; central heating and water heating installations result in far fewer fires.

Information drawn from the FPA large fire analysis for 1988 is shown in Figure 17. Again, the importance of the three main causes already described should be noted; arson, smokers' materials and matches and electrical sources of ignition cause about two-thirds of large fires. Arson is the largest single known cause of major fires. The actual proportion of fires due to arson may be even higher due to the number of large fires for which a cause is never discovered.

No definitive statistics can be quoted for office buildings specifically. However, the FPA has carried out a study of 31 fires in office buildings and banks that each resulted in a loss exceeding £250,000 between 1982 and 1986. In nine of these fires, the cause was recorded as arson. Other known sources of ignition were electrical appliances and equipment (eight fires), cutting, welding and blowlamps (four fires), and smokers' materials (one fire). Again, the significance of operations undertaken by contractors should be noted in the case of these very serious fires.

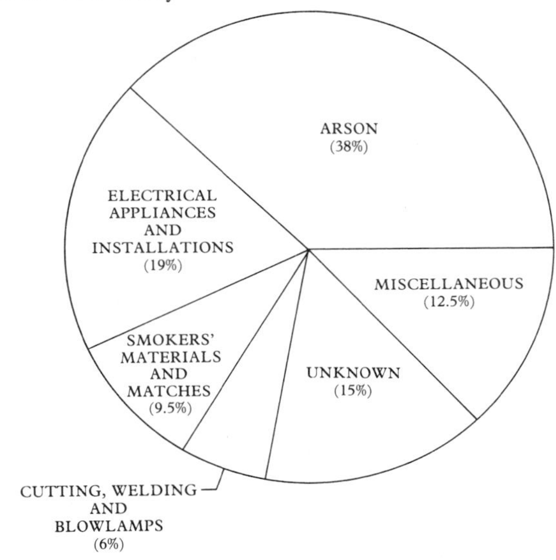

Figure 17: Causes of large fires

Companies with numerous locations should keep in-house records of all fire losses, including any very small fires that did not result in significant damage. Such records could allow the identification of hazards before a serious loss results.

Futher Reading

1. *Fire Statistics United Kingdom.* Published annually by the Home Office.

Chapter 4

The Scope and Nature of Fire Precautions

Earlier chapters of this book have described the common causes of fire and the threat that fire creates to people, property and the functioning of businesses. However, the remaining chapters, constituting the greater part of the book, are concerned with the response to the threat, in the form of *fire precautions*. Fire precautions may be defined as measures taken to reduce the probability that a fire may occur, and to mitigate the effects of any fire that does occur.

The scope of fire precautions is very wide. It extends, for example, well beyond the measures required by legislation. There are two reasons for this. Firstly, legislation is not generally concerned with the prevention of fire. The Health and Safety at Work Act, for example, does not, of course, permit positively unsafe situations for employees. Nevertheless, most fire-specific legislation is generally based on the assumption that a fire *will* occur, and requires that people be protected against injury when it does. For example, if a fire occurred every day in a building, it might reasonably be argued that the fire precautions were inadequate, but there would not necessarily be any breach of the Fire Precautions Act.

Secondly, legislation is concerned primarily with the safety of life and not with the protection of property or protection of a company's ability to function. Somewhat paradoxically, the measures required to protect life are often simpler, less extensive and usually less costly than those required to protect assets and earning capability, even though safety of life must always be the first priority. This is a natural consequence of the fact that, in most occupancies, people can be removed quite quickly from the hazards created by a fire, simply by evacuation of the building. (This is not, however, true of certain occupancies, such as hospitals.) The building, on the other hand, remains at risk until the fire is controlled and extinguished, as are many critical facilities, such as records, etc within the building.

There is a natural distinction between fire precautions that are intended to prevent the occurrence of fire and those that afford a degree of protection if fire does occur. It is conventional to refer to these two type of fire precautions as *fire prevention* measures and *fire protection* measures respectively.

Fire prevention

Fire prevention is defined in BS 4422 Part 1 as measures to prevent the outbreak of a fire and/or to limit its effects.

Fire prevention measures are very diverse in nature and include procedures as well as physical measures, to reduce the probability of the occurrence of fire. For example, fitting an earth leakage circuit breaker to an electrical installation may reduce the chance of a fire of electrical origin. Procedures for routine inspection of the electrical installation may also lessen the risk by leading to early identification and rectification of faults.

Fire protection

Fire protection is defined in BS 4422 Part 1 as design features, systems equipment, buildings, or other structures to reduce danger to persons and property by detecting, extinguishing or containing fires. Fire protection measures, therefore, are also very diverse in nature, and range, for example, from a brick wall to a sophisticated fire detection and extinguishing installation. These measures may be intended to *protect* any of three exposures—namely people, property and the ability of the organisation to function.

In fact, most fire protection measures tend to be grouped into those required for protection of life and those required for protection against financial loss; it is the former measures that are generally required by legislation, while the latter measures may be a requirement or recommendation of fire insurers, or be installed on the advice of in-house advisers. It is normally quite clear whether the provision of any fire protection measure is primarily related to life safety or property protection. Emergency lighting, for example may be an important life safety measure as it can assist in the evacuation of people, but it does little or nothing to reduce directly the risk of property loss. Similarly, a gaseous extinguishing installation may be installed to extinguish any fires in a computer suite, but is certainly not required to protect the occupants, who must be evacuated before the system is discharged.

Although it is usually possible to identify whether the primary function of a fire protection measure is life safety or property protection, there is invariably some overlap between the two objectives. A sprinkler system, for example, installed for property protection (see Chapter 12) will contribute to the life safety of persons in the building, particularly in parts distant from the area of fire origin. Fire resisting doors installed to protect the enclosure of a staircase in order to provide a safe escape route for occupants (see Chapter 6) will also, at a later stage in the fire, assist in the prevention of smoke and fire damage on floors above and below the floor on which the fire is located.

A more subtle distinction exists between fire protection measures that are installed to protect property directly and those intended to protect a particularly critical function on which a business depends. Some simple examples may make this distinction clear. First, consider a computer that controls a production process upon which the revenue earning capability of a manufacturing company depends. The computer may be highly protected against fire, perhaps by enclosure in a room with fire resisting walls, automatic fire detection and an automatic extinguishing system. The computer itself, however, may not be of high value and may, in any case, be insured against fire damage. However, loss of the computer may result in significant downtime of the production process and cause financial losses well in excess of the value of the computer. A more extreme example is the case of a critical real time computer facility which controls the operations at a larger number of locations. Fire damage to a few metres of communications cable, which may cost only a few pounds to replace, could result in huge losses to the organisation due to loss of communications with all remote locations.

As a further example, consider a quality control laboratory that contains specialist equipment that is used routinely to monitor the quality of products produced by a pharmaceuticals manufacturer. Again, loss of the laboratory may cause serious interruption to the manufacturing process.

It is thus clear that the purpose of fire protection measures can be divided into three categories; namely protection of life, protection of property or protection against interruption. However, the actual nature of the measure is frequently sub-divided into just two catagories, namely *active* or *passive*.

Active Fire Protection

Active protection measures inlcude mechanical and electrical equipment, such as fire detection, fire extinguishing and smoke control systems. Such systems actively respond in some manner when fire occurs. For example, in the event of fire, power is supplied to alarm sounders, water is caused to flow through pipes or a smoke extract fan starts up—the system has responded to the fire.

Passive Fire Protection

Passive fire protection measures, by contrast, are those which need not change in any manner in order to perform their fire protection function; they are inherently protective in their normal, everyday condition. Such measures are primarily associated with that part of the BS 4422 definition that relates to containing fires, but could also include good fire safety planning and design, adequate means of escape, compartmentation, structural fire protection and ventilation.

In practical terms, passive fire protection products are those which are mainly, but not solely, associated with building construction, linings, or contents, that have the objective of containing fire, or limiting the extent or rate of fire spread and development. The term encompasses a wide range of product types that are not necessarily of even vaguely similar nature. They may be as diverse as a fire resisting document storage cabinet, chemicals used to treat fabrics to improve their fire performance and paints used to reduce the surface spread of flame of timber linings, as well as the more traditional products, such as fire resisting building materials.

Passive fire protection has traditionally been regarded as the fundamental, basic form of fire protection, often specified at a very early stage in the design of a building. Active fire protection systems are sometimes regarded as "add-on" elements although it may be necessary to design active systems, such as sprinklers, at quite an early stage in the design process.

Pre-planning

Fire protection measures, by definition, only have a bearing on fire safety *after* fire has occurred and, therefore, fire prevention has failed. It has already been noted in this chapter that, while fire prevention measures comprise both procedures and equipment, fire protection measures involve only equipment and materials. There is, however, a further group of fire precautions that are concerned with the procedures, both short term and long term, that follow an outbreak of fire. These precautions may be described simply as pre-planning. Pre-planning covers planning for actions to be taken at the time of a fire, and planning for action after the fire.

Planning for actions in the event of fire includes the formulation of fire procedures (see Chapter 17) and the training of all occupants, including those with special duties in the event of fire. It also includes rehearsing the procedures by carrying out regular fire drills (see Chapter 18). Planning for action after a fire deals with the planning of salvage arrangements and the formulation of contingency plans for continuing the business. In the case of a hotel, for example, there might be a need to plan for accommodation of guests if the building cannot be reoccupied after the fire. In the case of a manufacturing company, it may be possible to formulate contingency plans for production to resume at another location.

Summary

Fire precautions may, therefore, be divided into three groups:

(a) fire prevention measures
(b) fire protection measures
(c) pre-plans for fire.

Many of the visible fire precautions in a building are fire protection measures. However, the "software" of fire safety, such as procedures to prevent fire and pre-plans for action in the event of fire, are just as important as the physical measures provided to prevent fire and protect against its consequences.

It is also important to note that the formulation of appropriate fire precautions in a building is a management duty (see Chapter 15). Fire precautions must not be an issue left to others, such as enforcing authorities or fire insurers, to impose on the organisation.

Chapter 5

Fire Prevention

The Importance of Fire Prevention

The prevention of fire, if successful, is more effective than merely minimising the effects of fire. Strangely, however, fire prevention is often overlooked in favour of fire protection. Even the fire prevention officers of a local authority fire brigade spend most of their time dealing with fire protection measures. Yet fire prevention is often a matter of simple common sense and need not always involve sophisticated measures or high technology. Perhaps it is because many fire prevention measures are almost trivial, that they are sometimes regarded by managers and qualified engineers as unworthy of their time and attention. In contrast, the level of engineering and capital expenditure associated with many fire protection measures make them of greater interest.

There is also a general impression that fires are inevitable, and that, therefore, only fire protection need receive attention. In this connection it is interesting to note the views of Mr. Desmond Fennell QC in his report on the investigation into the fire at King's Cross underground station in 1987, which resulted in the loss of 31 lives. The report states that:

> . . . the management remained of the view that fires were inevitable on the oldest and most extensive underground system in the world. In my view they were fundamentally in error in their approach . . .

and

> Dr. Ridley [then Chairman and Managing Director of London Underground Limited] . . . saw London Underground's key task as to minimise the risk of fires becoming a danger to passengers by a better control procedure and by removing materials which posed the greatest fire hazard. In effect he was advocating fire precaution rather than fire prevention.

It is my belief that this approach is seriously flawed because it fails to recognise the unpredictable nature of fire.

It is common, however, particularly after a fire disaster, to concentrate on fire protection defects, rather than inadequacies in fire prevention. After the fire at Bradford football stadium in 1985, when 56 people died, there were suggestions that football stadia should be sprinklered. It may be argued, however, that this serious fire could have been avoided by better housekeeping, so that the rubbish underneath the flooring of the stand (which it is supposed was ignited and led to the disastrous fire) was not present. Fire protection, therefore, only complements fire prevention; it must never be regarded as a substitute. Most fires are the result of a limited number of categories of ignition source (see Chapter 3). If it were possible to eliminate fires that result from arson, smokers' materials and electrical sources of ignition, the number of fires that occur in the United Kingdom would be dramatically reduced. Concentration on the prevention of such fires, therefore greatly diminishes the risk of fire in any premises. The remainder of this chapter deals with measures to combat these three sources of ignition, and other significant causes of fire.

Prevention of Specific Causes of Fire

Arson

Protection against arson involves measures that afford a high degree of security. While it is commonly believed that fire safety and security directly conflict, because of the possible detrimental effects of security measures on means of escape (see Chapter 6), good security is itself a fire prevention measure. Common security measures that are relevant to prevention of arson include the following:

(a) *Secure boundaries to prevent intruders.* In the case of a site, this involves the provision and maintenance of fences of adequate height and physical strength. For buildings, there is a need for all doors to be capable of being securely locked. This includes fire exits, for which suitable exit devices, such as panic bars, can be provided on the inside of the door. Security of windows should also be addressed.

(b) *Access control,* to ensure that only authorised personnel enter the premises, that they can only do so via supervised entry points and that they are properly identifiable. High risk areas within any site should be the subject of additional control.

(c) *Security lighting*, particularly in the case of open yards or large sites with open spaces between the perimeter fence and the buildings on site.

(d) *Intruder alarms*, to ensure that occupants may be alerted and the police summoned (usually by a remote monitoring centre) if unauthorised access to the premises is gained. For a large site or building, CCTV monitoring might also be appropriate.

(e) *Periodic patrols*, either by on-site security personnel or by a third party guarding company.

(f) *Vigilance by staff*, who should be aware of the need for security measures and be encouraged to challenge persons whom they consider may be unauthorised.

In assessing the risks, attention should not be paid exlusively to the large and dramatic fire—in a computer room even the most minor occurrence can have potentially disastrous consequential results.

In addition to these security measures, general good housekeeping contributes to the reduction of risk. Arsonists require fuel and are unlikely to bring this with them. Frequently, combustible waste and rubbish present a convenient fuel. These can be denied to an arsonist by their regular removal and proper disposal. Combustible goods, timber pallets, rubbish skips, etc should not be stored close to a building. An arsonist could, without even having to enter the building, start a fire that ultimately destroys the building. If combustible storage must remain in the open, it should be stored well away from any buildings. Flammable liquids are very useful to an arsonist as accelerants. All flammable liquid stores should be kept secure, and any large quantities should be removed from the workplace and replaced in the secure store at the end of the working day.

It has been asssumed, so far, that a potential arsonist is always an outsider. While this will normally be the case, there is also a need for precautions against arson by employees or others, such as outside contractors, with a genuine need to be on the premises. Arson by disgruntled employees or ex-employees, for example, is a genuine threat. This is more difficult to control but highlights the need for proper vetting of employees and following up of references. It should also be ensured that facilities for access by an employee cease as soon as the employee leaves the service of the company.

Management should analyse, and remain aware of, the extent of the threat of arson to their company. This will vary from one organisation to another, and depend on factors such as:

(a) *The nature of the organisation.* Large, faceless, establishment-type organisations may be seen as a more legitimate target than a small local family business. Schools are a particular target for vandals, who may set fire to the premises.
(b) *The activities of the organisation.* Potential target organisations are, for example, those associated with experiments on animals or trading in animal products, those with financial interests in, or major trading relations with, certain foreign countries whose policies are strongly opposed by radical pressure groups, etc and those in some areas of the defence industry. Also, one can never discount arson as a means of industrial sabotage.
(c) *The "softness" of the target.* Certain types of premises are inherently more vulnerable than others. The bus operating industry, for example, periodically suffers a major loss, invariably due to ignition of seats within parked vehicles; bus garages are often difficult to secure because there is a need for regular access for vehicles until late at night, and it is common for large numbers of vehicles to be parked in such close proximity that fire can spread readily from one vehicle to another.
(d) *Labour relations.* An organisation with good industrial relations is likely, by definition, to have fewer disgruntled employees.
(e) *Geographical location.* Premises in inner city areas are often at greater risk.

Liaison with the local police can assist in an awareness of the potential threat, and assist management in formulating an appropriate level of protection. The specialised nature of security will often require expert advice on the subject of both physical and electronic security measures. Advice should be sought from the crime prevention officer of the local police force and the company's insurers and insurance brokers. Advice may also be obtained from specialist consultants, who may be able to offer more in-depth guidance on certain matters.

Electrical Faults

Much can be done to prevent fires of electrical origin without an in-depth knowledge of electrical engineering. Fires of electrical origin can be divided into three groups, according to whether they involve:

(a) the fixed, permanent electrical installation in the building
(b) temporary wiring and leads to portable electrical appliances
(c) electrical appliances.

A modern electrical installation, installed and maintained in accordance with good practice, should not present a risk unless it is abused, inadequately modified or mechanically damaged. It is important, therefore, that all installation work, including the design of any new installation or modifications to an existing installation, complies with the relevant edition of *The Institution of Electrical Engineers Regulations for Electrical Installations* (currently the 16th edition) (more commonly known as the "IEE Wiring Regulations"). These Regulations, contrary to the implications of the title, have no statutory force in England and Wales. (In Scotland, electrical installations are required to comply with the Wiring Regulations by the Technical Standards that accompany the Building Standards [Scotland] Regulations 1990.)

However, compliance with the Regulations (in the case of installations to which they apply) would be likely to prove that the relevant requirements of the Electricity at Work Regulations 1990 have been satisfied. Compliance with the Regulations is also deemed to satisfy the requirements of the Electricity Supply Regulations 1988, which prohibit an electricity supply being provided to a consumer unless the installation is safe. The Wiring Regulations are primarily concerned with safety, particularly in respect of protection against fire and electric shock.

Fires may be started by any of the following.

(a) Overloading of cables by currents that the cables are not designed to carry; the cables then overheat and the life of insulation is shortened. This may occur because the current required by the appliances connected to the installation will, when the appliances operate normally, demand too much current. Abnormal conditions, such as an excessive mechanical load on a motor, or faults in equipment, can also be a cause of overload.

(b) Short circuit of conductors due to, for example, mechanical damage to insulation; the vast currents that may then flow may be thought of as a very extreme case of overload, and the heat that results will cause combustible insulation to burn.

(c) Leakage of current to earth, due to failure of the cable insulation.

(d) Loose connections, which result in local overheating of components, cables or combustible materials.

(e) Arcs and sparks that result from electrical faults.

(f) Overheating of cables due to the presence of thermal insulation; the cable insulation may then deteriorate and a fire can result.

An important part of the Wiring Regulations is devoted to avoidance of fires, using fuses or miniature circuit breakers to protect against the overcurrents that arise from overload or short circuit. The Regulations require that the currents at which these devices will isolate the circuit, must be matched to the current carrying capacity of cables. The maximum current that the Regulations permit a cable of a particular size to carry is related, in part, to the maximum temperature at which the insulation will be safe (although there are also constraints on voltage drop along the cable).

De-rating (ie, reduction of the maximum permissible current that the cable may carry) is required where semi-enclosed (rewirable) fuses are used as protection against overcurrents; these devices are slower to operate than cartridge fuses or miniature circuit breakers. De-rating of cables is also required if the cables are surrounded by thermal insulation, because heat produced in the cable cannot be readily dissipated. It should also be noted that PVC insulated cables should not be laid in contact with polystyrene (sometimes used for thermal insulation) as the plasticiser will migrate from the PVC, causing the insulation to become brittle and a hazardous situation to result.

Residual current devices

Fuses and miniature circuit breakers cannot protect against the leakage of very small currents between the cable conductors and earth. This may occur due to minor cable damage or the onset of failure of the cable insulation. Such small currents can cause local overheating and a fire. However, the circuit protection will only be tripped when sufficient current is drawn to cause adequate overcurrent. Nevertheless, it is possible to protect against small earth leakage currents by means of a *residual current device* (RCD). This device compares the current in the neutral and live conductors of a single phase circuit; these currents should be the same under normal circumstances. Any "out of balance" current represents leakage to earth. At a pre-determined value of this current, the RCD isolates the supply automatically.

This type of protection is required to protect socket outlets that are intended to supply outdoor electrical appliances, and may be used more generally to provide a high standard of protection against electric shock and fire. Devices intended to protect against the risk of shock (the most common function of the RCD) are set to operate when a leakage current of 30mA is detected. In some installations, an RCD can, however, lead to nuisance tripping due to the normal leakage through insulation and certain electrical equipment. A higher value of tripping current, such as 100mA, may still be adequate to protect against the risk of fire, and will be less subject to nuisance tripping. Expert advice should be sought before selecting and installing an RCD in industrial and commercial premises, etc. Where RCDs are installed, regular testing of the devices is important.

Installation and maintenance

Electrical design, installation and maintenance work should only be carried out by competent, qualified persons. The National Inspection Council for Electrical Installation Contracting (NICEIC) publish a roll of approved contractors, who undertake to carry out work in accordance with the Wiring Regulations, and their work is subject to periodic inspection by the NICEIC. In addition, the Electrical Contractors' Association (ECA) operate a guarantee scheme for the work of their member companies, whereby work that does not comply with the safety requirements of the Wiring Regulations will be rectified.

Maintenance, inspection and testing of electrical installations contribute to fire safety. Proper maintenance of electrical installations is a legal requirement, and it should be ensured that a designated person is responsible for the installation. There should be complete records of the installation, updated when modifications take place. It is unfortunate that many companies fail to arrange for routine inspection and testing of electrical installations. Yet this is an excellent way of ensuring that the installation remains safe by early identification of, for example, poor insulation.

Temporary installations

Installations on a construction site, and temporary installations, present a greater risk than permanent fixed installations. The wiring of such installations is likely to be more exposed to mechanical damage, and would not be supported in the same manner as a permanent installation. Appliances are also more likely to be subject to abuse. Although the Wiring Regulations do not require the same degree of support for cables in temporary installations as may be found in a permanent installation, it is still required that there be no strain on joints or termination. Temporary installations should be inspected and tested every three months. It is important that the cables used are suitable for the environment to which they are exposed.

Electrical appliances

Leads to portable appliances are more exposed to damage than fixed wiring. The electrical installation layouts of many office buildings are often not designed for the number of appliances that are now required in the modern office. As a result, it is common to find trailing leads and multiple adaptors in these buildings. Such practices should be avoided as far as possible. Long leads create even greater exposure to damage, and multi-way adaptors increase the potential for both overload and bad connections that may lead to overheating.

This should be taken into account during safety inspections. Where the practice is found to be prevalent, consideration should be given to the installation of additional socket outlets and the use of modern cable management techniques, including readily adaptable conduit systems. If adaptors must be used, the type that comprises a portable bank of sockets, connected to a lead with a plug on the end, should be used in preference to adaptors that plug straight into a socket outlet. If cable reel extensions are used for portable tools, no cable should remain on the reel while the tool is switched on. Otherwise overheating of the cable may result.

In the course of safety inspections, all leads to portable appliances should be checked visually. It should be ensured that the connections to plugs are tight and that the cord grip makes good contact with the outer sheath of cables, which should not be stripped back to expose the insulation of the conductors. Cables that are damaged should be replaced rather than repaired; the safety of a lead to a portable appliance should not depend on a piece of insulating tape. Joints in the cable should be avoided. If the cable is not long enough, it should be replaced with a longer cable.

Electrical appliances are themselves associated with a significant number of fires of electrical origin. Faults in the equipment are not, however, the sole cause of such fires; incorrect use of electrical equipment is also an important factor. Many types of electrical equipment produce heat when operating normally, and must be kept well clear of readily combustible materials. Electric fires are an obvious example, but precautions are also required in the case of, for example, soldering irons and incandescent light fittings. Proper stands should be provided for soldering irons, and a neon indicator light should be fitted to all sockets that are used for such sources of black heat.

Most of the electrical energy that is fed into a tungsten filament lamp is actually converted into heat and not light. A clear space must, therefore, be maintained around light fittings. Although fluorescent fittings do not create a great deal of heat, faults in the associated control gear have led to a number of fires; these should, therefore be mounted on a non-combustible surface. Some equipment, such as motors, must be continuously ventilated to prevent a rise in temperature; ventilation must not be obstructed.

All electrical equipment should be kept clean, and not be permitted to come into contact with grease, oil, waste materials, etc. There should be a proper maintenance schedule for all items of electrical equipment. Employees should, generally, not be permitted to bring their own electrical appliances, such as heaters, radios, etc into the premises. If the use of personal electrical appliances is permitted, they should first be checked for safety and compliance with relevant standards, and should be subject to the same maintenance as other electrical appliances in the building. All equipment should be switched off, and preferably unplugged, at the end of the working day unless its continued operation is essential. This practice applies even if the equipment itself is considered to be of low risk, as many appliances are. In areas such as workshops that contain a large amount of electrical test equipment, or rooms that contain numerous appliances, such as visual display units, a single local isolator should be provided so that all appliances can be simultaneously switched off. All equipment should be subject to a brief visual inspection during the course of any safety audits.

Smokers' materials

It is now common for smoking to be prohibited in many places of work purely on health grounds. Even if no blanket prohibition exists, there may be designated areas where smoking has been prohibited as a result of a ballot among the areas' occupants. This is one factor contributing to the contrast between statistics on fires caused by smokers' materials in domestic dwellings, and those in non-domestic buildings. In the 10 years from 1978 to 1987, the number of such domestic fires rose steadily in dwellings from 8600 in 1978 to a peak of 11,300 in 1985, falling to 10,200 in 1987. (These figures include fires caused by children playing with matches, which result in numerous domestic fires.) However, over the same period in non-domestic buildings, the number rose only slightly from the 8100 fires in 1978, peaking at 8500 in 1980, after which the number continued at an average of around 7700 fires per annum, dropping in 7200 in 1986 and 6800 in 1987, the lowest for 10 years (see Figure 18).

Carelessly discarded cigarettes, cigars, pipe tobacco and matches are all capable of starting a fire, but cigarettes are a greater risk than cigars and pipes. Cigarette lighters are safer than matches, simply because no discarded materials are involved. Ignition of various solid combustible materials by smokers' materials is possible although, other than in the case of a match that is burning, there is unlikely to be immediate flaming, but rather smouldering that can undergo a transition into flaming after some time. However, a cigarette can act as an immediate source of ignition for highly flammable vapours or gases.

Smoking should be prohibited in any areas where discarded smokers' materials are likely to act as a source of ignition, where a fire could develop unnoticed, and where even a small fire could result in a significant loss. For example:

(a) areas in which flammable liquids or gases, or combustible dusts, may be present, either under normal or abnormal circumstances; smoking should be prohibited within a specified radius of these hazardous areas
(b) areas in which large amounts of combustible storage, wastes, packing materials, etc are present
(c) warehouses, storage areas, stockrooms and loading bays

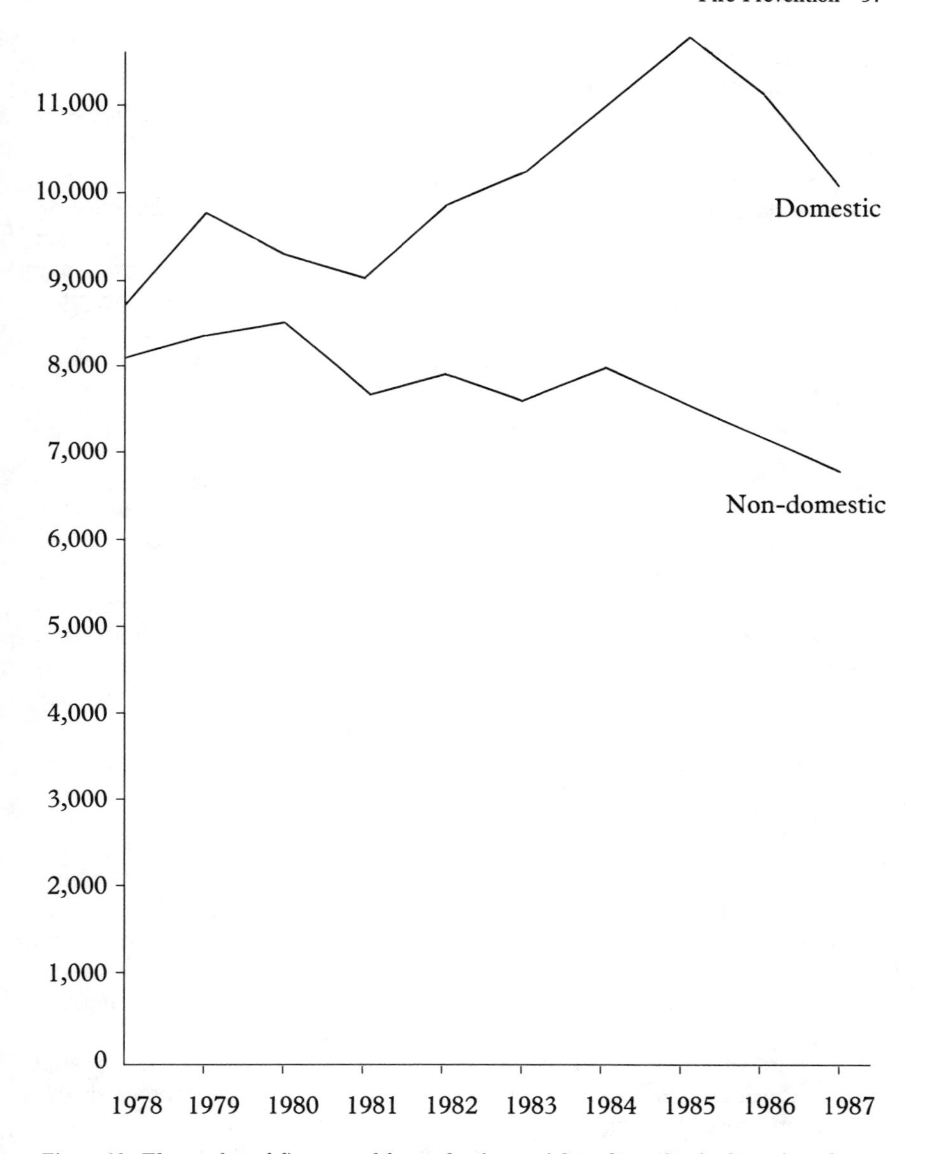

Figure 18: The number of fires caused by smokers' materials and matches in domestic and non-domestic buildings

(d) plant rooms
(e) infrequently visited areas
(f) computer rooms and rooms housing sensitive electronic equipment.

It is important that any rule that prohibits smoking is properly enforced. This is necessary regardless of whether the prohibition is for the purpose of fire safety or health. Employees will not necessarily distinguish between the two, and failure to enforce health-related smoking prohibition may encourage employees to smoke in areas in which smoking is prohibited for reasons of fire safety. Moreover, there is likely to be an absence of ashtrays for safe disposal of smokers' materials in any areas in which smoking is prohibited.

Prominent signs should be located in all areas where smoking is prohibited, and at the entry points to such areas (see Chapter 9). Ashtrays should be located adjacent to the signs at the entry points. The locations of no smoking areas should be clearly outlined, both in writing and verbally, as part of fire safety training (see Chapter 18), with the reason for the prohibition explained.

It must be accepted, however, that some people find it very difficult to abstain from smoking for prolonged periods. If there is a widespread prohibition of smoking in the premises, there is a danger of surreptitious smoking, which is likely to occur in the worst possible locations; namely those that are out of sight and in which, therefore, a fire may develop without discovery. To avoid this, a designated smoking room(s) should be provided. This may not need to be dedicated to the purpose of smoking, but may, for example, be a rest room, unless there are objections to this from some employees on health grounds.

Such rooms should be enclosed in fire resisting construction, and furniture and furnishings should be resistant to cigarette or match ignition. Linings should be non-combustible or of low flammability. The design of any chairs should be such that a cigarette cannot be trapped down the back of the seat. There should be suitable means for disposal of smokers' materials, and notices should be located at the exit(s) to remind people of the need to extinguish all cigarettes before entering the surrounding no smoking area. Consideration should also be given to the need for automatic fire detection, possibly using heat detectors (see Chapter 10).

In all areas in which smoking is not prohibited there should be adequate provision of ashtrays, preferably of a type in which the discarded materials are enclosed and on which a cigarette can be safely rested. Ashtrays should be emptied regularly, and certainly at the end of the working day, into suitable receptacles for disposal outside the building. The contents of ashtrays should not be mixed with other wastes, particularly if these are combustible. Staff should be encouraged not to put smokers' materials in general waste bins, and to avoid discarding combustible wastes into ashtrays or other receptacles intended for smokers' materials. It is desirable that smoking should be prohibited 30–60 minutes before the end of the working day.

Heating

It will be recalled from Chapter 3 that central heating installations appear to cause less fires than local heating appliances. This is reflected in the Loss Prevention Council's (LPC) scheme for classification of heaters for underwriting purposes. The LPC divide methods of heating into six classes; A being the safest and F the least safe. Classes A and B are less likely to attract any penalty in fire insurance premiums than those of lower classes; most central heating systems would come into Classes A and B.

Fixed heating installations are safer than portable heaters, which should be avoided if at all possible. Electrical installations supplying electric heaters should comply with the Wiring Regulations and should be installed by competent persons. Gas appliances should be installed in accordance with the Gas Safety (Installations and Use) Regulations 1984, which do not apply to factories but may be used as general guidance for installations in factories. The appliances should be installed by a contractor registered with the Confederation for the Registration of Gas Installers (CORGI). Any heating appliances in areas in which flammable liquids or gases may be present should be of a suitable type.

Sensible use of heating appliances could do much to prevent fires. A clear space should be kept around all sources of heat, so that combustible materials cannot be ignited and there is free circulation of air. Adequate guards may be required to ensure this. There should be no combustible construction in close proximity to hot flue pipes. Local appliances should be fixed to a non-combustible surface.

If portable heaters must be introduced for short term heating problems, radiant heaters should be avoided. Heaters should be sited where they cannot be overturned or mechanically damaged, and be positioned on a non-combustible surface well clear of any combustible materials. All heating appliances should be subject to regular inspection and maintenance. Staff should not be permitted to bring their own heating appliances into the premises.

Cooking

Sensible use of cooking appliances is necessary if fire hazards are to be minimised. Appliances should never be left unsupervised, and staff should be properly trained in the use of the appliances and action in the event of fire. The kitchen should be kept clean, and build up of grease deposits should not be permitted. A clear space should be kept around each appliance and, in particular, between deep fat fryers and other appliances. There should be clearly labelled facilities to shut off power, fuel and extract in an emergency.

Electric appliances should be installed by a competent person, such as an NICEIC approved contractor, in accordance with the Wiring Regulations. Gas appliances should be installed in accordance with the Gas Safety (Installation and Use) Regulations and BS 6173 (Installation of gas catering appliances), by a CORGI registered installer. All appliances should be regularly inspected and maintained. Grease filters, extract ductwork and grease traps should be subject to regular cleaning.

Deep fat fryers should be regarded as a particular hazard, as these are a common cause of cooking fires in non-domestic premises. As well as thermostats with a maximum setting of 205°C, there should be a high temperature cut out in case of thermostat failure. Grease traps should be fitted to any low level ductwork. There should be a facility to shut down the lids of fryers in the event of a fat fire. The risk of a fire associated with deep fat fryers is such that consideration should be given to a fixed manual/automatic fire extinguishing system (see Chapter 12).

Contractors' operations

Carelessness by outside contractors is a common cause of fire, including many fires that result in serious financial loss. In Chapter 3, cutting, welding and use of blow lamps were identified as particular sources of ignition. Not all of these fires would have been caused by outside contractors. It has been estimated, however, that perhaps 20–25% of all non-domestic fires result from "on-going work", such as refurbishment, repair and construction.

In 1990, a major fire occurred in part of the major Broadgate development in London during the final stage of its construction programme. This fire which, it has been suggested, resulted in one of the largest insurance claims in Europe for ten years, is believed to have started in a sub-contractor's office facility. A report on the fire by the Steel Construction Institute concluded that many more fires occur in temporary accommodation on building sites than is generally recognised and that comprehensive guidance on fire precaution measures, adopted during the construction phase, are required as a matter of urgency.

The range of hazards that contractors may, directly or indirectly, introduce to a building encompass most, if not all of those discussed in this book so far. They include:

(a) flammable liquids, such as adhesives, paints, thinners, timber preservatives
(b) flammable gases, such as acetylene and liquefied petroleum gases
(c) hot work, such as cutting, welding and use of blow lamps
(d) temporary electrical installations
(e) combustible materials, sometimes finely divided, eg sawdust and wood shavings
(f) careless disposal of smokers' materials by the workforce
(g) exposure to arson due to breaches in physical security
(h) burning of waste
(i) temporary heating appliances
(j) temporary lighting
(k) temporary buildings, partitions and screens of combustible construction
(l) tar boilers.

The hazards are exacerbated in buildings that are undergoing construction or major refurbishment, in which there may be incomplete floors and walls, inadequate fire stopping, incomplete means of escape and unserviceable fire alarm and sprinkler systems.

Fire safety requirements should form an integral part of the contract between a client and contractor. Ideally, a company should produce its own standard fire precautions for use in all contracts. Companies that have no such conditions may wish to cite *Standard fire precautions to be taken by contractors engaged on building and engineering works and maintenance for the Department of the Environment Property Services Agency*, available from HMSO. The Loss Prevention Council also intend to publish recommendations for fire prevention during contractors' operations in the near future. Contract conditions should cover matters such as:

(a) *Waste Removal*:
All combustible wastes should be removed regularly to a safe place away from the building. Burning of waste should take place at a safe distance from the building.

(b) *Flammable Liquids*:
Bulk stocks should be kept in a suitable secure location, outside the building. Quantities stored inside the building should be kept to a minimum and should be stored in metal lockers. Highly flammable liquids and petroleum spirits should be stored in accordance with the relevant regulations.

(c) *Temporary Partitions*:
These should preferably be constructed of non-combustible materials or materials that have a low surface spread of flame (see Chapter 7).

(d) *Gas Cylinders*:
These should be stored in a secure compound outside the building. Cylinders should be kept in the upright position at all times, and be removed from the building at the end of the working day. Liquefied Petroleum Gas (LPG) should not be introduced into basement areas.

(e) *Hot Work*:
A permit-to-work should be required for all hot work, such as cutting, welding and the use of blowlamps. A sample of a permit which is available from the Fire Protection Association is reproduced in Figure 19. The permit is signed by an authorised person only after ensuring that the work cannot be carried out off site, that the proposed location is safe and that all suitable precautions have been implemented. The area should be checked again on completion of the work, and 30–60 minutes following completion.

Areas in which work is to take place should be kept clear of combustible materials as far as possible. Remaining combustible materials should be protected with non-combustible screens or covers, and all holes in the surrounding construction should be protected to prevent entry of sparks. Two persons should be present at all times, at least one of whom should have training in first aid fire fighting. Fire extinguishers or hose reels should be kept at hand. Flashback arrestors should be fitted to the cylinders of cutting and welding equipment.

(f) *Tar Boilers*:
Tar boilers should be kept away from combustible materials and never be left unattended. There should be a permit to work system for their use and the area should be provided with ample fire extinguishing appliances. Tar boilers should not be used on roofs unless absolutely necessary.

(g) *Workmen's Huts*:
These should be kept well away (eg at least 10m) from buildings if possible, and an adequate clear space should be maintained between huts. Spaces beneath huts should be enclosed so that rubbish cannot accumulate below the hut.

(h) *Temporary Electrical Installations*:
These should comply with the relevant requirements of the Wiring Regulations, and be inspected and tested every three months.

(i) *Temporary Lighting Installations*:
Lamps designed for installation in the pendent position should not be installed in an upright position. All lamps should be kept well clear of any adjacent combustible materials.

(j) *Temporary Heaters*: These should be removed when not required. When present, they should be installed on non-combustible surfaces. General space heaters should preferably be fixed in position and kept clear of any combustible materials.

(k) *Security*:
It should be ensured that security is maintained during contractors' operations.

(l) *Smoking*:
If permitted, smoking should cease at least 30 minutes before the end of work on site.

(m) *Combustible Materials and Packaging*:
These should be stored in a suitable location, preferably in a hut 10m away from the building under construction/renovation.

The above precautions are not intended to be exhaustive and, if formulating detailed contract conditions, the reader is advised to consult the references contained in the bibliography at the end of this chapter.

HOT WORK PERMIT

(Not necessarily applicable to a normal production process)

APPLIES ONLY TO AREA SPECIFIED BELOW

BUILDING . . . . FLOOR. . . . . . .

NATURE OF THE JOB (INCLUDING EXACT LOCATION) . . . .

. . . .

THE ABOVE LOCATION HAS BEEN EXAMINED AND THE PRECAUTIONS LISTED ON THE REVERSE SIDE HAVE BEEN TAKEN.

DATE. . . . . *TIME OF ISSUE OF PERMIT. . . . *TIME OF EXPIRY OF PERMIT. . . .

SIGNATURE OF PERSON ISSUING PERMIT . . . .

SIGNATURE OF PERSON TO WHOM PERMIT IS ISSUED . . . .

*(It is not desirable to issue hot work permits for protracted periods; for example, fresh permits should be issued where work carries on from morning to afternoon).

TIME STARTED . . . . .TIME FINISHED

FINAL CHECK UP

Work area and all adjacent areas to which sparks and heat might have spread (such as floors above and below and on opposite sides of walls) were inspected continuously for at least one hour after the work was completed and were found fire safe.

SIGNATURE OF EMPLOYEE CARRYING OUT FIRE WATCH. . . . .

AFTER SIGNING RETURN PERMIT TO PERSON WHO ISSUED IT

Figure 19: Typical hot work permit (available from the Fire Protection Association)

PRECAUTIONS

(The person carrying out this check should tick as appropriate)

☐ Where sprinklers are installed that these are operative.

☐ Cutting and welding equipment in good repair and adequately secured.

PRECAUTIONS WITHIN 15m OF WORK

☐ Floors swept clean of combustible materials.

☐ Combustible floors protected by wetting down and covering with damp sand or sheets of non-combustible material.

☐ All wall and floor openings covered with sheets of non-combustible material. All gaps in walls and floors through which sparks could pass covered with sheets of non-combustible material.

☐ Where work is above floor level, non-combustible curtains or sheets suspended beneath the work to collect sparks.

WORK ON WALLS OR CEILINGS

☐ Combustible constructions protected by non-combustible curtains or sheets.

☐ Combustibles moved away from opposite side and clear of any metal likely to conduct heat. (Where metal beams are being worked on, and extend through walls or partitions, precautions must be take on the far side on such a wall).

WORK ON ENCLOSED EQUIPMENT (Tanks, containers, ducts, dust collectors etc.)

☐ Equipment cleaned of all combustibles.

☐ Containers free of flammable vapours.

FIRE WATCH

☐ Provision for the attendance of an employee during and for one hour after completion of work. Such employee being supplied with extinguishers or small bore hose and trained in the use of such equipment and in sounding an alarm.

SIGNATURE OF PERSON
CARRYING OUT THE ABOVE CHECK ....

Figure 19 (continued)

Industrial Processes

The measures discussed above would, if successful, contribute to the elimination of around 80% of all fires in non-domestic premises. However, in industrial premises, this figure drops to 60%. The reason for this is that many industrial processes give rise to fire hazards. Many of these hazards are unique to individual industries, and can only be addressed in terms of specific process controls.

However, some hazards are common to a number of industrial operations. These include:

(a) shrink wrapping
(b) battery charging
(c) paint spraying
(d) heat treatment
(e) drying
(f) use of flammable liquids and gases
(g) presence of combustible dusts.

Quite detailed fire prevention guides are available for such hazards. In addition, codes of safe practice are available for specific industries. The Loss Prevention Council produces a large number of guidance documents, which are applicable to most of the common risks described above and to some specific industries, such as cake and biscuit manufacturing. Other useful guidance documents include those produced by the Health and Safety Executive and by industry trade associations. Consideration of industrial process hazards is outside the scope of this book. However, it should be borne in mind that basic good housekeeping can make a contribution to reducing the fire risk in even the most high technology industries.

The Contribution of Furniture and Furnishings to Fire Prevention

In approximately eight per cent of non-domestic fires, the materials which ignite first comprise furniture and furnishings, floor coverings, blinds, upholstery, bedding and textiles. Although not a high percentage, it is equivalent to the same number of fires in which flammable gases constitute the item ignited, and involves more fires than those in which flammable liquids are associated with ignition. Furthermore, it should be compared with the seven per cent of fires that involve ignition of the building structure and fittings—even though the fire performance of building elements is much more strictly controlled than that of furniture and furnishings.

There is, therefore, a good case for controlling the ignitability and flammability of furniture, furnishings, etc particularly as legislative control is only exercised over these items in a very limited number of premises, such as places of entertainment. In the case of existing furniture and furnishings, it may be difficult to assess, or indeed modify, the fire performance. However, purchasing specifications for new goods should always include requirements on fire performance.

Domestic furniture flammability has received much attention in recent years because of its alleged role in domestic fire deaths, and is controlled by the Furniture and Furnishings (Fire) (Safety) Regulations 1988, as amended. These impose requirements on the flammability of domestic furniture and beds. However, the Regulations do not apply to non-domestic furniture. There is a need, therefore, for the purchaser to specify appopriate requirements. Guidance on the appropriate requirements is contained in BS 7176 (Specification for resistance to ignition of upholstered furniture) and BS 7177 (Specification for resistance to ignition of mattresses, divans and bed bases).

These standards divide occupancies into four hazard classes—low, medium, high and very high. Ignition resistance performance is specified for each hazard class by reference to the tests contained in BS 5852 (Fire tests for furniture) Parts 1 and 2 or, in the case of bedding, BS 6807 (Methods of test for the ignitability of mattresses with primary and secondary sources of ignition). Advice is contained in BS 7166 and BS 7177 on likely classifications of occupancies, such as offices, hotels, public buildings, hospitals, schools, etc. Factors to take into account in final classification of premises are also outlined. These include:

- the number of occupants and their ability to escape unaided
- the presence of automatic fire protection systems
- the presence of special hazards
- the location of the hazard area
- the effectiveness of staff control over evacuation.

If ignition resistance is imparted by chemical treatment, it is necessary to ensure that this is resistant to cleaning processes.

It is possible to specify fire performance characteristics for other items of furniture and furnishings by reference to various British Standard and other tests. However, in the case of tests for which results are not expressed as a simple pass/fail, there is less guidance on the level of performance that should be specified, than in the case of furniture and bedding. The appropriate standards to which reference should be made in purchasing specifications are listed below:

(a) *Bedcovers and pillows*:
BS 7175 (Methods of test for the ignitability of bedcovers and pillows by smouldering and flaming ignition sources). This standard uses the ignition sources of BS 5852 to assess the ignitability of pillows, quilts, mattress cases and covers, sheets, pillowslips, blankets, bedspreads and quilt covers—individually and in combination. Guidance on the flammability performance requirements that should be specified will be produced by the British Standards Institution in due course.

(b) *Curtain materials and blinds*:
BS 5867 Part 2 (Specification for fabrics for curtains and drapes. Flammability requirements). This standard gives three sets of performance criteria by reference to tests specified in BS 5438 (Methods of test for flammability of vertically oriented textile fabrics and fabric assemblies subject to a small igniting flame). The standard relates to the fabric from which curtains and blinds are made. Reference may also be made to two Crown Suppliers standards, which relate to made up curtains and blinds—FTS 7 Methods of test for assessing the ignitability of curtains, and FTS 17 Methods of test for assessing the flammability of internal window blinds by a flaming ignition source.

(c) *Carpets*:
Two tests exist: BS 4790 (Method for determination of the effects of a small source of ignition on textile floor coverings [Hot metal nut method]) and BS 6307 (Method for determination of the effects of a small source of ignition on textile floor coverings [methenamine tablet test]). A further standard, BS 5287 (Specification for assessment and labelling of textile floor coverings tested to BS 4790) sets out

the requirements for a carpet to be described as low radius of effects of ignition when tested in accordance with the hot metal nut method.

Excellent guidance on fire performance of furniture and furnishings for hospitals is contained in *Health Technical Memorandum (HTM) 87 (Firecode: textiles and furniture)*, available from HMSO. This guidance document recommends performance levels and safety measures for the complete range of furniture and furnishings that may be found in a hospital. The guidance can also be of assistance in other occupancies where high fire safety standards for furniture and furnishings are required.

Further Reading

1. Fire prevention in any occupancy is largely related to the activities associated with the occupancy. Attention is, however, drawn to the publications of the Health and Safety Executive and those of the Fire Protection Association, the latter of which can be purchased as a six volume "compendium of fire safety data". A number of industry trade associations also produce documents on safety.

Chapter 6

Means of Escape

Means of escape is defined in BS 5588 (Fire precautions in the design, construction and use of buildings) as:

> Structural means whereby a safe route is provided for persons to travel from any point in a building to a place of safety without outside assistance.

Means of escape is, therefore, the most fundamental of those fire precautions required for safety of life, and must be planned at an early stage in the design of a building. It should be noted from the definition that means of escape comprise structural measures; a lift, for example, could not be regarded as an adequate means of escape, even if the lift were designed for operation in the event of a fire. Similarly, lowering lines, folding ladders and chutes are not generally acceptable and do not, by definition, constitute adequate means of escape. The words "without outside assistance" should also be noted; rescue by the fire brigade must be discounted in planning means of escape. Similarly, escape onto flat roofs, or similar structures, from which there is no route to street level, other than rescue by ladder, does not constitute a means of escape.

Normally, "a place of safety" will be the open air. The Fire Safety and Safety of Places of Sport Act 1987 makes it clear that escape must terminate in a place of safety beyond the building. It is not adequate for occupants to discharge from the building into an adjoining alleyway or small yard, from where there is no escape, and in which the occupants remain at risk.

First Principles of Means of Escape

The most fundamental principle of escape route design is that people should be able to turn their back on a fire, and walk away from the fire towards safety wherever practicable (see Figure 20).

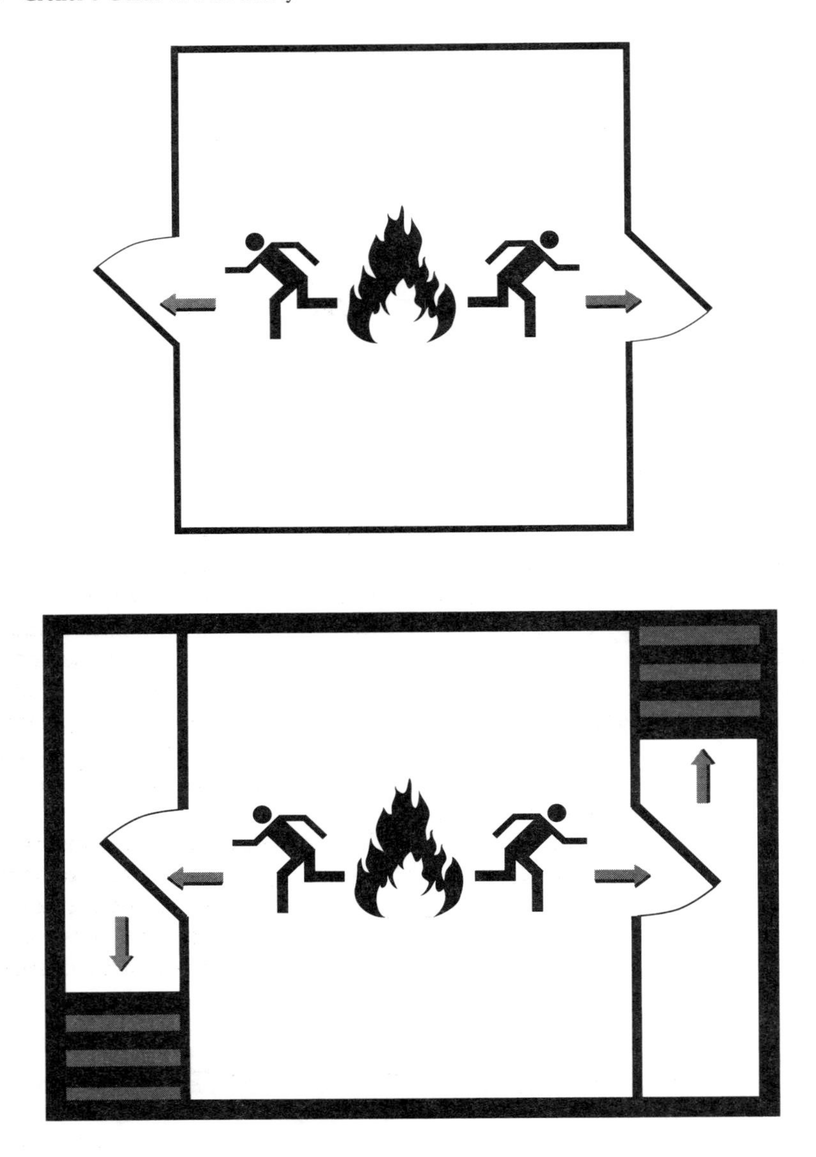

Figure 20: First principle of means of escape

It should be noted immediately that this will not be practicable in a small room, in a building with only one staircase, or within a corridor that leads to a "dead end", or indeed in any other circumstances where dead ends exist (see Figure 21).

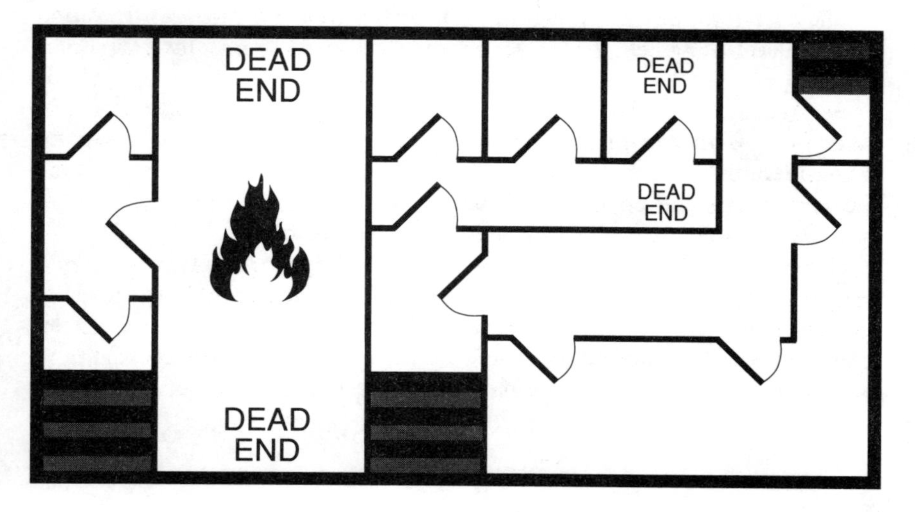

Figure 21: "Dead ends" – these are only acceptable in certain circumstances and are subject to special requirements (see text)

Escape in only one direction should be avoided where possible, but is acceptable in limited circumstances. However, to avoid the risk that people's escape route may be cut off by the fire *alternative escape routes* should generally be available.

Alternative escape routes are defined in the relevant part of BS 4422 (Glossary of terms associated with fire) as:

> Escape routes sufficiently separated by either direction and space, or by fire resisting construction, to ensure that one is still available should the other be affected by fire.

In a room or storey of a building, two exits are only considered to be alternatives if, from any point, the angle between the exits is at least 45° ("the 45° rule"). In order to understand the reason for this rule, consider the top diagram in Figure 22. The exits are very close together; common sense dictates that they cannot be regarded as alternatives, as one fire could easily prevent use of both exits. Clearly, the situation is much better in the lower diagram, in which the separation between the exits is acceptable. If the two exits are moved closer together, there comes a point between the two extremes at which the safety of the lower diagram is replaced by the hazard in the upper diagram. It is convention to regard this transition as the point at which the angle between the exits from any position is 45°.

As stated above, the escape routes must ultimately lead to a place of safety—invariably open air outside the building. However, as it may be a considerable distance between, for example the upper storeys of a multi-storey building and open air, it is normally necessary to first reach a *place of relative safety*, such as a protected staircase (see below).

Escape routes should be obvious to all building occupants, and should not be tortuous or complicated. People will be more confident in using escape routes that are part of the normal circulation routes. For example, there may be a reluctance to use an escape route through an adjoining occupancy, even although this may satisfy the requirements of legislation.

Design Codes

There are a number of very detailed codes of practice for the design of means of escape. The most important of these are as follows:

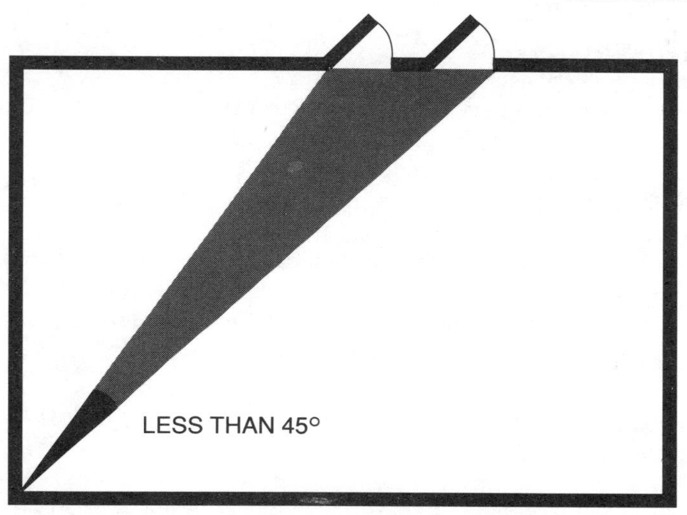

TWO EXITS – BUT NOT ALTERNATIVES

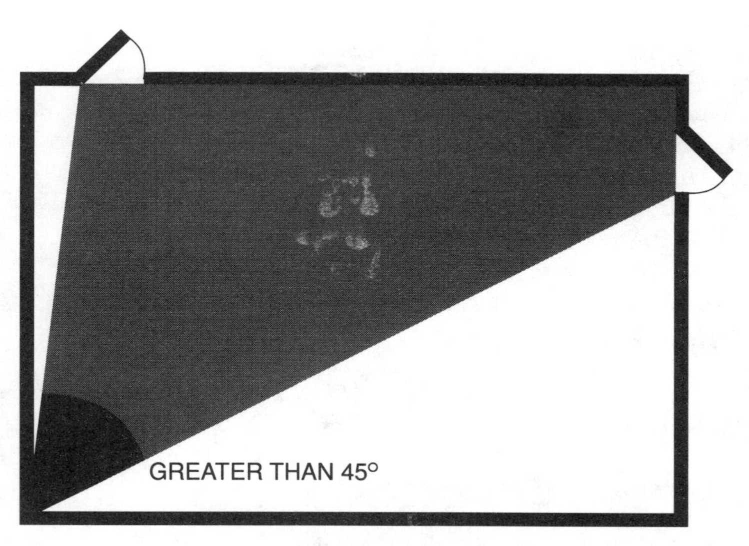

TWO ALTERNATIVE EXITS

Figure 22: The 45° rule

British Standards

BS 5588 (Fire precautions in the design, construction and use of buildings).
Part 1. Code of practice for residential buildings.
Part 2. Code of practice for shops.
Part 3. Code of practice for office buildings.
Part 8. Code of practice for disabled people.
(As discussed in Chapter 1, British Standard CP3 Chapter IV Part 1: 1971 and BS 5588 Section 1.1: 1984, although now replaced by BS 5588 Part 1, are made mandatory by current Building Regulations for flats/maisonettes and dwellinghouses of three or more storeys respectively.)

Home Office/Scottish Home and Health Department Guides

Guide to Fire Precautions in Existing Places of Work that Require a Fire Certificate. Factories, Offices, Shops and Railway Premises. HMSO, ISBN 0 11 340906 0. *Code of practice for fire precautions in factories, offices, shops and railway premises not required to have a fire certificate.* HMSO, ISBN 0 11 3409004 4. *Guide to Fire Precautions in Premises used as Hotels and Boarding Houses which Require a Fire Certificate.* HMSO, ISBN 0 11 341005 0. *Guide to Fire Precautions in Existing Places of Entertainment and Like Premises.* HMSO, ISBN 0 11 340907 9. *Draft Guide to Fire Precautions in Existing Residential Care Premises.* HMSO, (289a) Dd 8301909 C150 1/83 G3927. *Draft Guide to Fire Precautions in Hospitals.* HMSO, Dd 8302530 C20 6/83 (1264).

Home Office/Department of the Environment/Welsh Office Guide

Guide to Means of Escape and Related Fire Safety Measures in Certain Existing Houses in Multiple Occupation. HMSO, ISBN 0 86 252369 9.

Department of Health Codes

Health Technical Memorandum 81. Firecode: Fire precautions in new hospitals. HMSO, ISBN 0 11 321082 5. *Firecode. Nucleus Fire Precautions Recommendations.* HMSO, ISBN 0 11 321117 1. *Health Technical*

Memorandum 88. Guide to fire precautions in NHS Housing in the Community for Mentally Handicapped (or Mentally Ill) People. HMSO, ISBN 0 11 320801

Department of Education and Science Building Bulletin

Building Bulletin 7. Fire and the design of educational buildings. HMSO, ISBN 0 11 270585 5.

This may, at first seem a daunting list of documents, but closer inspection will reveal that each document is specific to a particular occupancy. In the case of offices, shops and hospitals, separate codes apply to new and existing buildings. There is, therefore, no problem of overlap between the areas of application, and in practice there is very little ambiguity as to which code should be applied to any particular building.

It should be noted that BS 5588 is intended to apply only to new buildings, or buildings undergoing extension or substantial modification, whereas the Home Office guides apply to existing buildings. This reflects the legislative situation described in Chapter 1, whereby responsibility for fire safety design of new buildings lies with the building control department of the local authority, but fire precautions in most existing buildings are enforced by the fire authority, or by other agencies that will consult the fire authority.

Means of escape codes are generally very prescriptive in nature. They set down relatively rigid requirements, although in theory at least, there should be flexibility in application. It is the matter of means of escape that causes the greatest contention between owners or occupiers and the enforcing authorities. A particular complaint is the absence of consistency between the requirements of one fire authority and another, and even between those of one fire prevention officer and another within the same authority.

Much of the detail in codes is based on experience, tradition and arbitrary limits to specified parameters, such as travel distances (see below). However, this does not detract from the fact that the existing approach to means of escape works in practice, and possibly errs on the side of safety.

With the notable exception of the code of practice for fire precautions in small factories, offices, shops and railway premises not required to have a fire certificate, the Home Office guides listed above are intended for enforcing authorities, although they are of value to architects, designers, consultants and others involved in work that might affect the means of escape in existing buildings. The code for non-certificated places of work was produced for building owners or occupiers because, in these non-certificated premises, it is the duty of the owner or occupier to ensure that the fire precautions are adequate, and the premises are not subject to routine inspection by the fire authority (see Chapter 1).

It might be expected that the design requirements for means of escape would be consistent in each code, at least as far as those relevant to similar premises are concerned. Unfortunately, this is not the case, and although differences might be considered to arise from subtle differences between occupancies, in truth, a number of the differences merely reflect the arbitrary nature of some requirements and the difference in thinking between the code-writers. Thus, there are certain differences between the recommendations of BS 5588 for means of escape in new offices or shops, and the recommendations of the corresponding Home Office guide.

Anomalies also exist within certain codes. For example, in the case of houses in multiple occupation, different escape route requirements arise according to whether the premises are considered to constitute a hostel or be divided into self contained units. Although many houses in multiple occupation can be readily grouped into one category or the other, the differences in the requirements are not necessarily soundly based. Moreover, there are houses in multiple occupation that are difficult to categorise—such as a house that is used to accommodate university students, which may be regarded as a student hostel or self contained flats, according to the mere degree of communal facilities.

The sections that follow concentrate on the basic principles of means of escape and ignore various differences between the detailed recommendations of the various codes, except where these differences relate to fundamental principles. It is advisable, therefore to consult the relevant code for more detailed guidance and seek the opinion of the enforcing authority or suitably qualified fire safety specialists.

Principal Aspects of Design

In planning means of escape, or assessing its adequacy in an existing building, there are three major elements to consider:

(a) travel distances (or, alternatively, direct distances)
(b) escape route and exit capacities
(c) the number of occupants for whom means of escape must be provided.

The requirements of these parameters will have a major bearing on the configuration and number of staircases and exits.

Travel Distance, Direct Distance and Floor Space Factors

Travel distance may be defined as the distance to be travelled from any point in a building to the nearest:

(a) final exit (ie an exit to a place of safety, normally the open air)
(b) door to a protected staircase (see below)
(c) door to an external escape route (eg an alleyway, balcony, bridge, walkway, flat roof, etc).

Thus, travel distance is the maximum distance that a person would have to walk to reach a place of relative safety or to reach open air, measured along the actual route they would follow. Codes specify maximum travel distances in order to minimise the exposure of people in the unprotected part of the escape route to the effects of fire. Although these travel distances should not be applied too rigidly, they should not generally be exceeded.

At the design stage of a building, final internal layouts and furnishings will not normally be known. It is, therefore, not possible to measure travel distances, as the exact escape route along which people will travel may not be finalised, and may become convoluted by internal partitioning. Thus, BS 5588, which applies to new work, offers the alternative of measuring the *direct distance*. Direct distance is defined as:

> The shortest distance from any point within the floor area, measured within the external enclosures of the building, to the nearest storey exit, ignoring walls, partitions and fittings, other than the enclosing walls or partitions to protected stairways.

Direct distance is, therefore, a form of "as the crow flies" straight line, between the furthest point in the accommodation and the storey exit. The limits that BS 5588 recommends for direct distances are two-thirds of those specified for travel distances. This permits the shortest distance that a person may travel from the furthest point to the point of protection to be increased by 50% as a result of partitioning and furnishings.

The maximum permitted travel distance varies a little from one code to another. Within any one code, very different travel distances are normally specified according to whether there is escape in one direction only (ie a dead end), or alternative means of escape (escape is possible in more than one direction). In addition, different travel distances apply to areas in which the fire hazard varies from the normal hazard of the occupancy. Maximum travel distances recommended in the most popularly used codes for common places of work, such as offices, shops and factories are shown in Tables 3–5. For other occupancies, the relevant code should be consulted.

CODE	ACCOMMODATION	MAXIMUM TRAVEL DISTANCE/(OR DIRECT DISTANCE) SPECIFIED FOR:	
		ESCAPE IN ONE DIRECTION	ESCAPE IN MORE THAN ONE DIRECTION
BS 5588 Part 3	General office areas	18m (12m)	45m (30m)
	Ancillary accommodation (eg rooms containing hazards such as boilers, transformers, switchgear, fuel storage, generators, etc)	6m	12m
Home Office Guides	Normal risk offices	18m (limited to 12m within a room enclosure)	45m

Table 3: Travel distances for offices

CODE	ACCOMMODATION	MAXIMUM TRAVEL DISTANCE/(OR DIRECT DISTANCE) SPECIFIED FOR:	
		ESCAPE IN ONE DIRECTION	ESCAPE IN MORE THAN ONE DIRECTION
BS 5588 Part 2	Most shops	18m (12m)	45m (30m)
	Small ground storey shop with a single exit	27m (18m)	
	Ancillary Accommodation (eg rooms containing hazards such as boilers, transformers, switchgear, fuel storage, generators, walk-in cold store, etc)	6m	12m
Home Office Guides	High Risk	12m (limited to 6m within a room enclosure)	25m (limited to 12m within a room enclosure)
	Normal Risk	18m (limited to 12m within a room enclosure)	30m

Table 4: Travel distances for shops

CODE	ACCOMMODATION	MAXIMUM TRAVEL DISTANCE SPECIFIED FOR:	
		ESCAPE IN ONE DIRECTION	ESCAPE IN MORE THAN ONE DIRECTION
Home Office Guide for Premises that require a Fire Certificate	High Risk	12m (limited to 6m within a room enclosure)	25m (limited to 12m within a room enclosure)
	Normal Risk	25m (limited to 12m within a room enclosure)	45m (limited to 25m within a room enclosure)
	Low Risk	45m (limited to 25m within a room enclosure)	60m
Home Office Guide for Premises that do not require a Fire Certificate		25m	45m

Table 5: Travel distances in factories

Staircase and Exit Capacities

Limitation of travel distance alone does not ensure the adequacy of means of escape. In a crowded shop, for example, a single, narrow exit door might be insufficient to enable all occupants to escape quickly enough to be safe from any fire that develops—even though no occupant were greater than the maximum specified travel distance from the exit. The number and width of exits and staircases, therefore, must be sufficient to enable sufficiently rapid evacuation.

The principles involved in calculating the required number and width of exits are based on a very simple model. It is traditionally assumed that the shoulder width of an adult is around 0.53m. Therefore, any exit of this width, which is known as a *unit of exit width*, will only permit people to pass through in single file. It is further assumed that a column of people passing through an exit in single file do so at the rate of 40 persons a minute. In practice, an exit of only 0.53m width would be somewhat tight for occupants to pass through and, therefore, a factor of safety is normally added to this figure; thus, BS 5588 requires a width of 0.9m to cater for around 40 persons a minute, while the Home Office Guide for places of entertainment recommends that the width of a single exit door should be not less than 0.75m.

In principle, however, a unit of exit width is capable of discharging 40 persons a minute. Moreover, any exit that is less than two units of exit width can still only permit people to discharge in single file at this rate. When a width of two units is reached, the discharge capacity effectively doubles as people can, according to this simple model, pass through two at a time. Thus, in principle, an exit that is 1.06m in width should be capable of discharging 80 persons a minute.

If the required evacuation time is then defined, it is possible to calculate the number of occupants that may be served by any exit. Based on experience and studies of major fires, an evacuation time of two and a half minutes is traditionally deemed to be required. (A contributing consideration in the evolution of this time is often held to be a fire at the Empire Theatre, Edinburgh in 1911 when an audience of 3000 evacuated safely in around 2½ minutes—allegedly the time taken for the band to play the National Anthem during the evacuation!). Thus, in theory, one unit of exit width is adequate for evacuation of 100 persons, while an exit of two units caters for 200 persons.

Recommendations for exit widths and escape routes in most codes are based on the above model, although the figures in some codes have been rounded off or modified slightly, resulting in minor variations. In BS 5588, the relationship between exit width and discharge capacity is as shown in Table 6.

DISCHARGE CAPACITY (NUMBER OF PERSONS)	EXIST WIDTH (METRES)
50	0.8
110	0.9
220	1.1
240	1.2
260	1.3
280	1.4
300	1.5
320	1.6
340	1.7
360	1.8

Table 6: Exit and escape route capacities recommended in BS 5588

It should be noted that, in the case of 220 persons and above, the figures in Table 6 are based on 5mm per person. In the case of places of entertainment, the Home Office Guide adopts a more traditional approach, based on a unit of exit width of 525mm, and increases in exit width above two units are made in increments of 75mm, which are deemed to cater for 15 people. The Guide also recommends three different evacuation times, namely two minutes, two and a half minutes and three minutes, according to the type of construction of the building.

In the case of staircases, the same principles apply, but the situation is complicated by the fact that allowance is made for the number of persons who can be accommodated within the staircase itself. For example, if a staircase serves only one floor, its capacity, as specified in BS 5588, will be as outlined in Table 6. If it is now extended to a second floor, its capacity must be greater, constituting the original capacity plus the standing capacity between the original floor and the additional floor. Mathematically, this becomes quite complicated, but staircase capacities, based on an evacuation time of two and a half minutes, are tabulated in BS 5588, and these are reproduced in Table 7.

In the case of high office buildings, it may not be necessary to evacuate all floors of the building simultaneously. Provided staircases are approached

DISCHARGE CAPACITY (number of persons)									
NO. OF FLOORS SERVED	WIDTH OF STAIRCASE								
	1000mm	1100mm	1200mm	1300mm	1400mm	1500mm	1600mm	1700mm	1800mm
1	150	220	240	260	280	300	320	340	360
2	190	260	285	310	335	360	385	410	435
3	230	300	330	360	390	420	450	480	510
4	270	340	375	410	445	480	515	550	585
5	310	380	420	460	500	540	580	620	660
6	350	420	465	510	555	600	645	690	735
7	390	460	510	560	610	660	710	760	810
8	430	500	555	610	665	720	775	830	885
9	470	540	600	660	720	780	840	900	960
10	510	580	645	710	775	840	905	970	1035

Table 7: Staircase capacities recommended in BS 5588

by way of a protected corridor or lobby, and suitable fire alarm and public address systems are installed, it may be acceptable to evacuate only two floors at a time. In this case, the aggregate width of all stairways may be reduced below the figures contained in Table 7. Guidance on such phased evacuation and the relevant staircase capacities is contained in BS 5588 Part 3.

It is necessary to build a degree of redundancy into means of escape. Accordingly, in calculating the total exit and staircase capacity of a building, it is always assumed that one exit/staircase is inaccessible due to the fire. The total exit capacity, therefore, must remain adequate for the number of occupants when each exit or staircase is discounted in turn.

It is often difficult to predict the likely number of occupants for whom means of escape must be provided. In this case, *floor space factors* may be used, ie the theoretical number of occupants may be calculated from the area of the accommodation, using figures relating to the floor space per person. For example, BS 5588 recommends that a figure of $5m^2$ per person be used for open plan offices, $7m^2$ per person for other offices, $2m^2$ per person for supermarkets, $30m^2$ per person for storage accommodation, and $0.3m^2$ per person in bars where people normally remain standing, etc.

Protection of Escape Routes

In defining travel distance, the terms *protected* staircase and *protected* lobby were used. In referring to means of escape, the term *protected* has a particular meaning. An escape route (or part of an escape route), such as a corridor or staircase, is *protected* only if it is enclosed (other than in the case of an external wall) by construction that is fire resisting.

The term *fire resisting* construction was discussed in Chapter 2. It refers to construction (walls, floors, ceilings, doors, etc) that can resist attack by fire for a specified time. For protection of means of escape, a fire resistance of 30 minutes is usually specified. However, longer periods of fire resistance may be required for high hazard areas, and may be required by Building Regulations to minimise fire spread as opposed to protecting escape routes. (Further discussion of requirements for fire resisting elements of construction may be found in Chapter 7). Not all escape routes are required to be *protected*, although it is a common misconception that all corridors should be enclosed in fire resisting construction (see below).

The Three Stages of Escape

Means of escape can be divided into three stages:

Stage 1—travel within rooms
Stage 2—horizontal travel to a storey exit or a final exit
Stage 3—vertical travel within a stairway and thus to a final exit.

It should be noted from Tables 3–5 that Home Office Guides for existing premises tend to make a particular distinction in the travel distance permitted within stage 1 and that permitted in stage 2, whereas BS 5588 tends to combine stages 1 and 2 for the purpose of travel distance limitation. The general requirements for offices, shops and factories, for each of the three stages are described below. However, for the specific requirements for any occupancy, the appropriate code should be consulted.

Stage 1: Travel within Rooms

(a) Room contents should be so arranged that there is free passageway to exits.
(b) The travel distance may be limited (see, for example Tables 3–5).
(c) "Large" rooms (often defined as those accommodating 50 persons or more) usually require more than one exit, so that there is an alternative exit if the route to one is blocked by fire. (Note that the 45° rule applies).
(d) The flammability of wall and ceiling linings is normally restricted (see Chapter 7).

Special requirements apply in the case of "inner rooms", defined as rooms from which escape is possible only by passing through another ("access") room. The purpose of these requirements is to ensure that the escape route for occupants of the inner room is not cut off by a fire in the access room before they can escape.

In the case of inner rooms:

(a) there must be either:
 (i) a clear vision panel between the inner and access rooms, so

that occupants of the inner room can see a fire in the access room, or
   (ii) a space between the top of the partitions between the inner and access rooms, or
   (iii) automatic smoke detection in the access room to give early warning of fire to occupants of the inner room
(b) there must be no inner rooms leading off other inner rooms (ie an inner room must not act as an access room for a further inner room)
(c) the access room must not be an area of high fire hazard.

Stage 2: Travel to a Storey Exit

Corridors with alternative means of escape

The requirements for cellular accommodation in which there are corridors with alternative means of escape are as follows.

(a) Each room should be fitted with a door (which need not be fire resisting or self closing, except in the case of sleeping accommodation) so that smoke movement can be prevented by closing the door.
(b) Except in the case of sleeping accommodation, the enclosing walls or partitions of the corridor need not generally be fire resisting or extend above false ceilings, but they should extend to any false ceiling to prevent smoke movement in the early stages of a fire.
(c) A travel distance limitation applies (see Tables 3–5).
(d) Codes frequently specify a minimum corridor width, which must be adequate for the number of occupants.
(e) Long corridors should be sub-divided by doors to separate staircases (so that more than one staircase is unlikely to be affected by smoke) and to limit the maximum length of corridor that may become smoke logged. These doors are usually permitted to have a fire resistance that is less than 30 minutes, but must be resistant to the passage of smoke (see Chapter 7). The doors may normally be held open providing they close automatically on operation of automatic smoke detectors or the building's fire alarm system.
(f) There should be adequate exit capacity for the number of occupants, assuming that one exit is not available.
(g) The 45° rule applies (see above).

(h) Doors should preferably open in the direction of escape, and must do so if a significant number of persons (eg 50 or more) is involved.
(i) The flammability of wall and ceiling linings in the corridors should be low (see Chapter 7).
(j) Escape routes should not be obstructed in width or contain fire hazards.

Dead End Corridors

The requirements for other corridors apply except that:

(a) the corridor should be a protected route, ie doors opening onto the corridor should be fire resisting, self closing and resistant to the passage of smoke; enclosing walls or partitions should be fire resisting and should extend from slab to slab through any false ceiling or floor
(b) a very limited travel distance applies (see Tables 3–5)
(c) at the point at which alternative means of escape are reached, the alternatives should be separated from one another by fire resisting self closing doors that are resistant to the passage of smoke. (See Figure 23.)

Open Plan Areas

(a) a travel distance limitation applies (see Tables 3–5)
(b) there should be adequate exit capacity for the number of occupants, assuming one exit is not available
(c) the 45° rule applies (see above)
(d) doors should preferably open in the direction of escape, and must do so if a significant number of persons (eg 50 or more) is involved
(e) the flammability of wall and ceiling linings is usually restricted. (See Chapter 7.)

Stage 3: Vertical Travel down a Staircase

(a) If the staircase is *protected*, it is a place of relative safety, and therefore there is no need for any limitations on travel distances within the staircase. In this case, doors to the staircase must be fire resisting

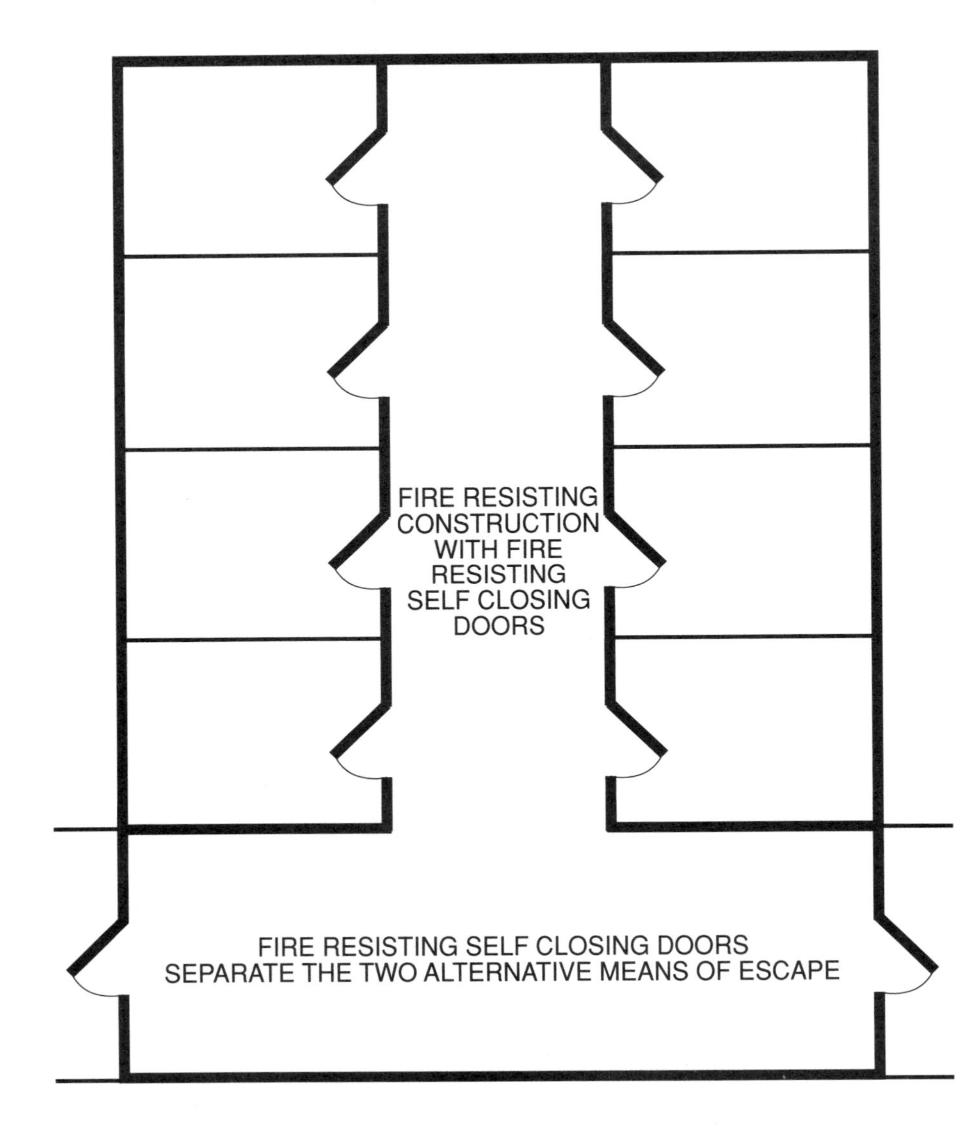

Figure 23: Requirements for dead ends

and self closing. The ability of staircase doors to fit well in their frames, and to protect against the penetration of smoke, is also very important. Many authorities do not permit staircase doors to be held open by units that release the doors automatically when fire is detected or the fire alarm system operates. Although some authorities permit such an arrangement in multi-staircase buildings, it is not an acceptable practice in a building with a single staircase.

(b) If the staircase is unprotected (such as an open staircase between two floors in a shop), it affords no degree of safety from a surrounding fire. Therefore if, in small premises, an unprotected staircase forms part of the means of escape (eg from the first floor of a small shop), the distance of travel down the staircase would, in effect, form part of the stage 2 travel distance. However, the presence of an unprotected staircase may not be acceptable at all in some premises. Even if an unprotected staircase does not form part of the means of escape, it is a route for vertical fire spread; it must, therefore, be ensured that the staircase is not detrimental to means of escape, and some codes limit the number of floors through which an unprotected staircase may pass.

(c) If a building is served by only one staircase, obviously dead ends are created, and the travel distance limitation, in effect, restricts the floor area of such a building. In addition, codes restrict the number of storeys, or height of building, that may be served by only a single staircase. In offices, for example, BS 5588 generally limits this arrangement to buildings that are not more than 11m in height and not more than three floors above ground level. It is normal to provide protected lobbies between a single staircase and the accommodation on each floor, so that fire and smoke must pass through two doors before they can affect the staircase.

(d) Staircase capacity must be adequate for the number of occupants, even if, in multi-staircase buildings, any one staircase is discounted on the assumption that it cannot be used due to the fire.

(e) It should not be necessary to pass through a staircase enclosure to reach an alternative escape route; nor should the only route from one part of the premises to another be through a staircase enclosure, as this will encourage the wedging of the staircase doors. In either case, by-pass arrangements should be provided.

(f) Ideally, a staircase should lead directly to a final exit. Otherwise, there should be two exits from the staircase enclosure, each leading to final exits via routes that are separated from one another by fire resisting construction. Alternatively, there should be a protected route to a final exit. Similarly, if there is more than one staircase without final exits within the actual protected enclosures of the staircases, the routes from each staircase should be separated.

(g) The flammability of any wall and ceiling linings must be negligible. (See Chapter 7)

(h) The staircase enclosure should contain no fire hazards or combustible materials.

(i) External staircases are usually permissible, but should, in effect, be protected routes. Thus, doors opening onto the stairways should be fire resisting and self closing, and windows in close proximity to the staircase should contain fire resisting glazing in frames that are fixed shut (see Chapter 7).

(j) Spiral staircases are only acceptable in certain circumstances, and for a limited number of persons. Vertical ladders are rarely acceptable unless, for example, they are the alternative means of escape from a plant room that is not normally occupied and is likely to be visited by no more than a very small number of persons.

(k) Escape in an upward direction should generally be avoided, but a short distance of travel to, say, a roof exit may be accepted in unusual circumstances, but not generally for members of the public. If exit across a flat roof is accepted, there are usually various special requirements. These include defined routes guarded with barriers, suitable roof construction, and the absence of any hazards, such as rooflights or ventilation outlets, through which fire could pass and cut off the means of escape.

(l) Self rescue devices, such as lowering lines, are not usually acceptable under any circumstances.

Final Exits

Ultimately, all escape routes lead to a final exit from the premises. Common requirements for final exits are as follows:

(a) The exits should be obvious and/or signposted.

(b) The exits must open easily. Security fittings for fire exits are discussed later in this chapter.
(c) Revolving doors are normally required to have conventional exit doors sited adjacent to them.
(d) In modern codes, wicket doors, goods delivery shutters and window exits are not normally acceptable as final exits, and are generally regarded as unsuitable for members of the public under any circumstances.
(e) On escape through a final exit, it must be possible to disperse from the building.

The Inter-relationship Between Means of Escape and Security

It is a commonly held belief that there is a direct conflict between requirements for security and those for means of escape. In a simplistic sense it is true that good security necessitates highly secure entrance and exit doors, whereas fire exits must be readily available for use in an emergency. However, in reality, this is a gross over-simplification, and potential conflicts between the two objectives can almost always be overcome without serious compromise of either life safety or security.

However, inadequate security equates to bad fire prevention; a high level of security actually contributes to fire safety. In addition, while safety of life from fire must, in case of real conflict, always override security requirements, the fire safety specialist must recognise that there can be situations in which overriding the security specialist's objectives can result in an overall increase in the risk to life. For example, in premises occupied by VIPs who are at risk from terrorists, and in banks and other premises in which the risk of armed robbery is high, no favour is done to the occupants by insisting that their safety from fire is so paramount that they must be exposed to the danger of being shot, blown up or kidnapped. There is often a need, therefore, for the fire specialist to consult with any security specialist who is involved with the building, to appreciate the level of the security threat and the form of security precautions that are required.

As stated above, when such consultation does take place, an adequate solution can normally be formulated. In considering the problems that arise, the following points should be borne in mind:

(a) Fire exits may be secured provided they can be opened readily from the inside in an emergency.
(b) Arrangements that involve the use of a key, such as the provision of a key in a glass fronted box adjacent to the exit door, are no longer regarded as acceptable. The key may be difficult to access or use if there is a crowd of people pressing against the exit door, or if visibility is reduced by smoke. In addition, those unfamiliar with the premises may believe the door is unopenable. One of the recommendations contained in the report of the committee of inquiry into the fire at Woolworths, Manchester in 1979 (which resulted in 10 deaths) was that the use of keys in glass fronted boxes for doors on escape routes should not be allowed in the future.
(c) The ideal form of fastening for a fire exit door is a panic lock or latch, which is released by pressure on a bar that runs across the full width of the door. Panic bars are not, however the only acceptable form of release mechanism. They tend to be required where the exit may be used by large numbers of persons (sometimes defined as 50 or more), particularly if the persons are members of the public. In other areas, the only requirement is that the devices used are simple and easy to use by occupants, and are able to result in immediate release of any locking device. Panic bolts tend to secure a door at two points, but security specialists normally require an arrangement whereby the risk of manipulation from outside is minimised; this will usually entail securing the door to the frame at the hinged edge.
(d) If the security of a fire exit door is a problem, consideration should be given to fitting an alarm device to the door so that a warning is given (locally and/or remotely) if the door is opened. This may, in complex buildings, be supplemented by CCTV monitoring.
(e) Electronic locking of doors may sometimes be acceptable provided adequate safeguards are implemented. This may include some of the following:
    (i) fail safe locks that release the door on power failure
    (ii) release of locks on operation of the fire alarm system
    (iii) a local electrical override control by each door that, once

operated, cannot be reset without replacement of a frangible element

(iv) a means for mechanically overriding the lock in an emergency.

(f) It may be acceptable to some enforcing authorities for normal fastenings, such as panic locks and latches, to be supplemented by additional fastenings, such as padlocks and chains, during periods of non-occupation, provided there is a reliable procedure for removing these as part of opening procedures before any public enter the premises. This arrangement may sometimes be found in theatres and cinemas.

(g) Since windows should not form part of the means of escape (unless, in exceptional circumstances, a proper window exit is provided for a small number of persons), bars on windows should not affect the means of escape. Even so, following a fatal fire at James Watt Street, Glasgow in 1968, enforcing authorities were advised to press for removal of bars in all cases where they are not strictly required for security purposes. Legislation does not, however, generally demand that windows are not barred. Nevertheless, bars on windows can impede firefighting operations, and may prevent rescue if the means of escape are, in very unusual circumstances, impossible for occupants to use. The report on the Woolworths fire reiterates the advice that followed the James Watt Street fire in this respect. The potential effect of window bars on fire safety is also recognised in the various parts of BS 8220 (Security of buildings against crime).

(h) Badly fitted, or inappropriate, locks and latches can impair the fire resistance of doors (see Chapter 7).

(i) It may be undesirable for certain fire resisting self closing doors to be self locking, eg the front doors of a flat.

Means of Escape for Disabled People

There is an increasing awareness in society that disabled people should be able, as a right, to enter and use modern buildings, whether to work, study and learn, be accommodated, or engage in leisure activities. Equally, once in the building, disabled people must be safe from fire. The right of access is now enshrined to some extent in Building Regulations, and the need for safe egress follows from this. It should be noted that disability can take many forms but, as this chapter is concerned only with means of escape, consideration of the requirements for disabled people relates primarily to non-ambulant people, particularly those in wheelchairs, although there is also a need to consider facilities for blind people.

Guidance on this subject is contained in BS 5588 Part 8 (Fire precautions in the design, construction and use of buildings. Code of practice for means of escape for disabled people). As in the case of other parts of BS 5588, the code is intended primarily for new buildings or buildings undergoing substantial refurbishment. However, an appendix to the code considers the application of the code to existing buildings. It is recognised that, in the case of an existing building, compliance with the code is not always possible. Nevertheless, it is recommended that alternative ways of meeting the objectives of the code should be sought. The code also stresses that non-compliance with its recommendations should not be regarded as adequate grounds for excluding disabled people from a building.

Much of BS 5588 Part 8 is concerned with structural measures to facilitate escape by non-ambulant persons in the event of fire. However, it stresses that management procedures are an essential part of arrangements for escape by disabled people. The procedures recommended include special arrangements for assisting wheelchair-bound persons, or others with walking difficulties, along corridors or stairways, and for supervising the use of an evacuation lift if provided (see below). An appendix to the code gives advice to management. The importance attached to procedures is consistent with BS 5588 Parts 2 and 3 (Code of practice for shops and Code of practice for office buildings) which, in the parts of the Codes made mandatory by Building Regulations, advise that building managements must make ad hoc arrangements for evacuation of chairbound persons.

A possible procedure is that nominated members of staff are made responsible for assisting in the evacuation of disabled people. A particular example of this is the "buddy" scheme, whereby a nominated person is responsible for assisting a designated disabled person who works in the vicinity. The advantages of this arrangement are that the able bodied person and the disabled person often work in the same department, can be made aware of each other's absence on any day, and can develop confidence in each other's ability to carry out rehearsed procedures in an emergency.

There is a need, however, to ensure that a deputy or deputies are nominated to take on the role when the nominated helper is absent, and that they are aware of their responsibilities when they arise. Perhaps a more serious disadvantage is that the freedom of the disabled persons may be restricted, as there may be no nominated helpers when they visit other parts of the building which, in the event of a fire, might not be able to be accessed rapidly by the nominated helpers. There may, therefore, be a need to train a proportion of, or all, fire wardens (see Chapter 17) in evacuation of disabled people.

Ideally, helpers should be trained to carry wheelchair-bound disabled people in their own wheelchairs. However, the weight of some motorised wheelchairs may make it necessary to provide specially designed "evacuation chairs" into which the disabled people are assisted by those helpers.

The code also introduces the concept of refuges. A refuge is defined as:

> An area that is both separated from a fire by fire resisting construction and provided with a safe route to a storey exit, thus constituting a temporarily safe space for disabled persons to await assistance for their evacuation.

It is a common misconception that the creation of refuges involves the provision of large, dedicated spaces that are enclosed in construction that will afford very long periods of fire resistance. The code makes it clear that this is not the case. A refuge is required to be of sufficient size only to accommodate a wheelchair and permit the wheelchair user to manoeuvre into the space without undue difficulty; the space required for the wheelchair is recommended as at least 700mm × 1200mm, which ideally ought to be increased to 900mm × 1400mm to allow space for manoeuvring. The code suggests that, in many buildings, such spaces will be formed as part of the design and construction process. Indeed, the code advises that the provision of refuges:

> ought normally to be possible both without affecting the internal design of the building to any material extent and without incurring substantial additional costs.

Examples of satisfactory refuges further clarify the simple nature of refuges. The examples comprise an enclosure, such as a compartment, protected lobby, protected corridor or protected stairway, and spaces in the open air, such as balconies or flat roofs, that are remote from the fire and provided with means of escape. However, it is stressed that the creation of refuges should not obstruct the flow of able bodied persons.

This is very important; arrangements for evacuation of disabled people must never impede the means of escape for able bodied people. However, compliance with the code should automatically result in buildings that offer enhanced means of escape for able bodied people. One important corollary is that if there are deficiencies in the means of escape for able bodied people, the means of escape are likely to be particularly inadequate for disabled people. Nevertheless, if staircase landings, lobbies or corridors are of sufficiently generous size and suitably protected they can, in principle, constitute refuges for disabled people without any further modification.

The code recommends that a refuge should be provided for each protected stairway on each storey, except for:

- single storey buildings
- storeys from which all exits are final exits
- storeys consisting exclusively of plant rooms
- buildings in single occupancy comprising not more than a basement, ground and first storey with a floor area per storey of $280m^2$ or less.

Prolonged periods of fire resistance are not required for the enclosures of refuges. A period of 30 minutes is recommended by the code.

The code also describes the technical requirements for evacuation lifts, which may be used by disabled people in the event of fire. A fire fighting lift that is intended for use by the fire brigade, and that complies with the requirements for such lifts, may be used as an alternative. In the case of evacuation lifts, the requirements include enclosure of the lift well in fire resisting construction, a recall-to-ground switch and, with minor exceptions, a secondary source of power supply, with cables that are separated from those of the primary supply.

It should be emphasised, however, that the code does not specifically recommend that evacuation lifts be provided in all buildings; the provision of an evacuation lift merely reduces, but does not eliminate, the need to arrange physical assistance for evacuation of disabled people by way of staircases. Even if an evacuation lift is provided, there is a risk that it may become defective or that it cannot be used for some reason. Accordingly, even in buildings with evacuation lifts, disabled people, having reached a refuge, must have access to a staircase.

Blind people can often manage to evacuate a building with which they are sufficiently familiar, with only minimal assistance. However, the design of lighting and emergency lighting should take the needs of partially sighted people into account, particularly in respect of the uniformity of lighting level. In addition, BS 5588 part 8 incorporates suggested aids to the use of staircases by blind people. These include:

(a) colour contrasting of stair nosings
(b) colour contrast between handrails and supporting walls
(c) tactile thresholds at the head and foot of each flight
(d) raised arrows on the handrails at upper storeys, indicating the direction of the nearest final exit storey.

Although many blind people have a remarkable ability to negotiate a building, in the event of fire they may have to use alternative means of escape with which they are not familiar. This should be taken into account in planning the evacuation of blind people.

In considering the evacuation of able-bodied people, the importance of dispersal away from the building has been stressed. Clearly, the same principle should apply to disabled people. They should not be placed at risk by their inability to move far enough away from the building. Furthermore, the siting of evacuation assembly points should take disabled people into account, so that they are able to reach the assembly point and are not placed at risk by so doing.

Checking the Means of Escape

The means of escape should be regularly checked (eg on a weekly basis) to ensure that it remains adequate. This should not be time consuming, particularly if a logical approach is adopted by following the three stages of escape. The use of simple checklists can be of assistance by acting as an *aide mémoire* for the non-specialist. Typical points to look for are listed below:

Rooms:

(a) is there ready access to exits? (large rooms may require access to more than one exit).

Corridors:

(a) are they free of storage/fire risks?
(b) if they are required to be protected, is the protection maintained?
(c) are all cross corridor doors:
  (i) adequately self closing? (including those normally held open but released automatically in the event of fire)
  (ii) not wedged open?
  (iii) of good fit?
  (iv) undamaged?

Protected Staircases:

(a) is protection maintained?
(b) are they free of storage and fire risks?
(c) are all doors:
  (i) adequately self closing? (including those normally held open but released automatically in the event of fire)
  (ii) not wedged open?
  (iii) of good fit?
  (iv) undamaged?

Final Exits:

(a) are they accessible?
(b) do they open easily?
(c) are they free of obstructions outside the premises?
(d) can occupants disperse away from the building?

Periodically, a more thorough examination of means of escape should be carried out. It should then be ensured that, for example:

(a) no unsuitable wall or ceiling linings have been erected
(b) fire stopping above false ceilings has not been breached
(c) no changes to internal layout have materially affected the means of escape
(d) there is no route for smoke spread around cross corridor doors.

Further Reading

1. *BS 5588 (Fire precautions in the design, construction and use of buildings).*

   Part 1. Code of practice for residential buildings.
   Part 2. Code of practice for shops.
   Part 3. Code of practice for office buildings.
   Part 8. Code of practice for means of escape for disabled people.

   (As discussed in Chapter 1, British Standard CP3 Chapter IV Part 1: 1971 and BS 5588 Section 1.1: 1984, although now replaced by BS 5588 Part 1, are made mandatory by current Building Regulations for flats/maisonettes and dwelling houses of three or more storeys respectively).
2. *Department of Education and Science Building Bulletin 7. Fire and the design of educational buildings.* HMSO ISBN 0 11 270585 5.
3. Department of Health. *Health Technical Memorandum 81. Firecode: Fire precautions in new hospitals,* HMSO ISBN 0 11 321082.
4. Department of Health Firecode. *Nucleus Fire Precautions Recommendations.* HMSO ISBN 0 11 321117 1.
5. *Department of Health Technical Memorandum 88. Guide to fire precautions in NHS Housing in the Community for Mentally Handicapped (or Mentally Ill) People.* HMSO ISBN 0 11 320801 4.
6. *Home Office/Scottish Home and Health Department Guide to Fire Precautions in Existing Places of Work that Require a Fire Certificate.* Factories, Offices, Shops and Railway Premises. HMSO ISBN 0 11 340906 0.
7. *Home Office/Scottish Home and Health Department Code of practice for fire precautions in factories, offices, shops and railway premises not required to have a fire certificate.* HMSO ISBN 0 11 340904 4.
8. *Home Office/Scottish Home and Health Department Guide to Fire Precautions in Existing Hotels and Boarding Houses that Require a Fire Certificate.* (In press)
9. *Home Office/Scottish Home and Health Department Guide to Fire Precautions in Existing Places of Entertainment and Like Premises.* HMSO ISBN 0 11 340907 9.

10. *Home Office/Scottish Home and Health Department Draft Guide to Fire Precautions in Existing Residential Care Premises.* (289a) Dd 8301909 C150 1/83 G3927. HMSO
11. *Home Office/Scottish Home and Health Department Draft Guide to Fire Precautions in Hospitals.* Dd 8302530 C20 6/83 (1264). HMSO.
12. *Home Office/Department of the Environment/Welsh Office Guide to Means of Escape and Related Fire Safety Measures in Certain Existing Houses in Multiple Occupation.* HMSO ISBN 0 86 252369 9.
13. Nelson J I A *Means of Escape from Fire in Buildings.* A design guide to the statutory requirements (England and Wales). Charles Knight Publishing.

Chapter 7

Building Construction

Structural fire protection is defined in BS 4422 Part 1 (Glossary of terms associated with fire) as "those features in layout and/or construction which are intended to reduce the effects of fire". Thus, structural fire protection involves the use of those passive fire protection products that are related to building construction (see Chapter 4).

The hazards of fire that structural fire protection is intended to limit are broadly those controlled by the Building Regulations (see Chapter 1), namely:

(a) collapse of the building
(b) spread of fire within the building
(c) flame spread over the linings of walls and ceilings
(e) spread of fire beyond the building.

To these may be added the spread of smoke within the building. The extent to which it is necessary to control these hazards, particularly fire spread, may be well beyond that required in order to satisfy the Building Regulations or, indeed, any fire safety legislation. Protection of property or critical facilities demands a higher standard.

Structural Stability: Fire Protection of the Structure

The relevant requirement in B3 of Schedule 1 to the Building Regulations 1985 states:

> The building shall be so constructed that, in the event of fire, its stability will be maintained for a reasonable period.

The effect of fire on the structural stability of a building is a very complex subject, involving a sound knowledge of structural engineering principles. However, one basic fire safety objective is perfectly clear: the probability of *structural collapse* (the inability of a loadbearing element of construction to continue to support its load) due to fire should be minimised.

In practice, elements of structure require a certain amount of *fire resistance* (see Chapter 2). For the purpose of Approved Document B, an element of structure includes any of the following:

(a) a member forming part of the structural frame of a building, or any other beam or column, but not a member forming part of a roof structure only
(b) a loadbearing wall or loadbearing part of a wall
(c) any floor other than the lowest floor of a building or a platform floor ("raised floor")
(d) a gallery or raised storage area that is less than one half the area of the space into which it projects
(e) an external wall
(f) a wall that separates adjoining buildings
(g) a wall that is provided to *compartment* the building (see below)
(h) a *protecting structure* (see below).

Tables in the Approved Document set out varying periods of fire resistance for elements of structure according to:

(a) the use of the building (different requirements apply to each of the nine "purpose groups", such as dwelling houses, flats, offices, shops, industrial buildings, etc into which occupancies are divided)
(b) the height of the building
(c) the maximum floor area of each storey, or compartment, of which the element forms part (see below for discussion of compartmentation)
(d) the cubic capacity of the building or the compartment of which the element forms part
(e) whether the element does or does not form part of a basement (including the floor over the basement).

However, it is most likely that the specification of fire resistance for elements of structure will be simplified in the revised Regulations.

Compliance with the Building Regulations in order to protect against structural collapse, may be insufficient to provide an adequate standard of property protection. Fire insurers might well desire longer periods of fire resistance, since building collapse would greatly increase the financial loss, and premium discounts could apply where elements of structure are adequately protected.

Insurers grade buildings according to the protection of the structure against fire damage. The Loss Prevention Council publish a document entitled *Rules for the construction of buildings grades 1 and 2*. A Grade 1 building has a relatively high resistance to fire and could qualify for premium discounts. A Grade 2 building is essentially non-combustible and is unlikely to attract any penalty in premium. Compliance with these rules does not ensure that the Building Regulations will be satisfied even though, in some respects, they impose requirements beyond those of the Regulations. When the Rules are updated, it is likely that their format will permit more ready comparison with the Building Regulations, so that it is more obvious as to which document contains the more onerous requirement for a particular application.

Protection Against the Spread of Fire and Smoke

Compartmentation by Walls and Floors

The relevant performance requirement for compartmentation, expressed in B3 of Schedule 1 to the Building Regulations states:

> The building, or the building as extended, shall be sub-divided into compartments where this is necessary to inhibit the spread of fire within the building.

In the context of the Building Regulations, compartmentation refers to the sub-division of a building by walls and/or floors for the purpose of limiting fire spread within the building. Approved Document B refers to the fire resisting walls and floors that are used to separate one fire compartment from another as "compartment walls and floors". The Approved Document specifies maximum compartment sizes for each type of occupancy in the form of maximum floor areas and volumes.

Compartment walls and floors need not (and generally cannot) be imperforate, as they are penetrated by service ducts and risers, staircases, lifts, escalators, etc. However, these penetrations must be enclosed in a protected shaft, of a construction that is of the same fire resistance as required for elements of structure. Doors in compartment walls or floors, and in the enclosing walls and floors of a protected shaft, are required to be fire resisting.

The compartmentation required by the Building Regulations is to prevent a major conflagration that would be beyond control by the fire brigade. Certain Local Acts (see Chapter 1) also specify maximum compartment sizes for large storage buildings; compartments beyond the sizes specified in these Acts are permitted only if there are additional fire protection measures, such as sprinklers, automatic fire detectors and smoke ventilation.

There are other objectives that give rise to the need for a form of compartmentation. Technically, the enclosure of any space, such as a small room, within a building by fire resisting construction constitutes compartmentation, even though the term "compartmentation" is often reserved for the division of a building into the relatively large compartments required by the Building Regulations.

Codes, such as BS 5588 (Fire precautions in the design and construction of buildings) recommend that certain high hazard areas within a building are enclosed in fire resisting construction. The periods of fire resistance recommended vary from 30 minutes for kitchens, workshops, low voltage equipment rooms and small storage areas, to no less than 60 minutes in the case of boiler rooms, high voltage equipment rooms, etc. Prolonged periods of fire resistance (as long as 4 hours in some cases) are also imposed by the requirements of Section 20 of the London Building Acts (Amendment) Act 1939 (see Chapter 1) for "special fire risk areas", such as underground car parks, basement loading bays, transformer sub-stations, etc. More generally, in premises where people sleep such as houses in multiple occupation, hotels and boarding houses, etc consideration of life safety demands fire separation between individual occupancies.

In order to limit property loss in the event of fire, fire insurers generally require that hazardous storage areas, such as those containing flammable liquids, hazardous processes (eg paint spraying) and fire risks (eg diesel generators and oil filled transformers) be separated from surrounding accommodation by fire resisting construction. Protection of property does not, however, only involve the creation of small compartments around special risks. Fire insurers also favour a broader form of compartmentation that is more akin to that required by the Building Regulations. The purpose is to limit the insurers' (and client's) estimated maximum loss (EML). This is defined as the maximum loss that is likely to occur in the event of fire, assuming that fire protection arrangements are effective. Classic applications for such compartmentation include:

(a) Separation of a manufacturing process from the raw materials and finished goods storage areas. (In the storage areas, the fire load is often high—although the fire inception hazard is normally lower than in the process area, the loss potential can be very great.)
(b) Sub-division of large warehouses. (Again, although the fire inception hazard may not be high, the loss potential can be enormous.)
(c) Separation of sprinklered parts of a building from unsprinklered parts.
(d) Separation of buildings that are likely to attract a high fire insurance premium from buildings that would be more favourably rated, eg separation of an office block from a factory area.

In order to protect the ability to function (ie prevent interruption to business) in the event of fire, it is often necessary to enclose a facility in fire resisting construction to prevent the spread of fire *into* the facility. The most common example of this principle may be found in the construction of a computer suite within a building. The enclosing construction is normally fire resisting to prevent fire spread from surrounding accommodation. Periods of fire resistance recommended by BS 6266 (Code of practice for fire protection of electronic data processing installations) range from one hour to four hours, according to the fire load of the adjacent accommodation. Facilities on which the computer equipment depends should, of course, be similarly protected.

Many organisations are now quite dependent on computer facilities, but there may be many other facilities that need to be protected in order to prevent interruption. These could include communications facilities, records, and patterns for a manufacturing process. In all such cases, the critical facility should be enclosed in fire resisting construction.

Sealing and Sub-division of Concealed Spaces

While it is important to protect against any form of unrestricted fire spread, concealed fire spread within cavities, such as roof spaces, floor voids and ceiling voids is a particular hazard. Concealed fire spread may permit fire to develop to an extent that it is a threat to life before evacuation takes place, it certainly increases the threat to property, and it may create difficulties for fire fighting by the fire brigade. Past experience, such as fires in schools that were constructed with undivided roof spaces, has demonstrated the hazards of cavities. The fire at the Summerland leisure complex on the Isle of Man in 1973, which resulted in 50 deaths, also graphically provided a further example of the problem—in this case a void between an external combustible wall and internal linings.

In 1976, the Building Regulations introduced requirements for cavities. The performance requirement of the current Regulations is set out in B3 of Schedule 1 to the Regulations, which states that:

> Concealed spaces in the structure or fabric of the building, or the building as extended, shall be sealed and sub-divided where this is necessary to inhibit the unseen spread of fire and smoke.

Accordingly, for each occupancy type, Approved Document B specifies that concealed spaces should be sealed and divided by *cavity barriers*. A *cavity barrier* is simply construction, which may already be provided for another purpose, to seal or sub-divide a cavity.

Doors

In terms of fire safety, doors may be required to perform any of the following functions, according to their location:

(a) prevent the spread of fire
(b) prevent the spread of smoke, particularly relatively cold smoke
(c) both (a) and (b).

Doors that afford a fire resistance of anything from 30 minutes to four hours are readily available. Those providing the shorter periods of fire resistance are normally of timber construction while, for the longest periods of fire resistance, steel is normally used. Timber doors tend to be used throughout commercial premises, except in the case of high hazard plant rooms and compartment walls of substantial fire resistance, where metal doors and shutters may be appropriate. Metal doors and shutters are also used in industrial premises to maintain the fire resistance of fire break walls and floors.

Modern timber fire resisting doorsets incorporate an *intumescent strip* in either the door or the frame. This swells at temperatures of, typically, 150°C and seals the gap around the edge of the door, which is the point at which an "integrity failure" (failure to resist the passage of flame) most commonly occurs. It is unlikely that a door would achieve a fire resistance of 30 minutes unless an intumescent strip is fitted. Many manufacturers insert a colour coded plug in the door edge to indicate the fire resistance and, if applicable, the need for an intumescent strip. Modern fire resisting doors need not be 45 mm thick, nor is there a need for 25 mm rebates, as were specified many years ago.

Older doors may not incorporate intumescent strips, and are thus unlikely to afford a fire resistance of 30 minutes if they were tested in accordance with modern test methods. They need not be replaced, however, unless the fit of the door in its frame is poor because, for example, the door has become warped. The decision as to whether an existing fire resisting door is acceptable will often lie with the relevant enforcing authority, who may be prepared to accept existing doors. Any new fire resisting door should obviously comply with modern requirements.

A smoke seal should be fitted to doors that are required to provide smoke control as well as fire resistance. This seal, which is similar to, or may actually be, a draught seal, will substantially reduce the amount of smoke that can pass through the door before the temperature is high enough to cause an intumescent seal to operate.

Although intumescent seals and smoke seals are available as individual components, combined intumescent/smoke seals are readily available, and are necessary for timber doors that are required to protect against the passage of both fire and smoke.

The degree of insulation afforded by some fire resisting doors, particularly those of metal construction, may be minimal, and in the event of fire they can become extremely hot on the opposite side to the fire. The thermal radiation emitted from this unexposed face can be sufficient to ignite combustible materials, which should not, therefore, be placed in close proximity to an uninsulated door.

There may be applications in which insulated doors would be of benefit. For example, the fire resisting door to a computer tape store should afford a good degree of insulation as, if there is a significant fire load in the surrounding accommodation, transmission of heat through the door could result in temperatures within the store that could cause damage to the tapes.

The ability to resist the passage of smoke may also be required for reasons other than life safety. For example, it is desirable for fire doors to rooms that contain sensitive electronic equipment to perform a smoke control function.

In modern codes, it is now conventional to specify fire doors by means of the letters "FD" followed by the required integrity in minutes. Thus, a 30 minute fire resisting door would be specified as FD 30. If the door is also required to fulfil a smoke control function, the suffix "S" is added (eg "FD 30S").

BS 5588 Parts 2 and 3, which relate to fire precautions in new office and shop buildings (see Chapter 6), contain the following performance requirements for doors:

(a) fire doors to protected stairways, lobbies etc: FD 30S
(b) dead end corridors: FD 20S
(c) ancillary accommodation, such as plant rooms: FD 30—FD 60 (according to the nature of the accommodation)
(d) lift shafts, except those within protected staircase enclosures: FD 30
(e) service shafts, etc: FD 30
(f) cross-corridor fire doors: FD 20S
(g) fire doors to external fire escape staircases: FD 30.

Approved Document B, which applies to virtually all types of occupancy, but is concerned with fire spread rather than means of escape, specifies the fire resistance of doors in the following manner:

(a) fire doors in a "separating wall" between occupancies: an equal fire resistance to the separating wall (minimum 60 minutes)
(b) fire doors in compartment walls separating flats or maisonettes from communal areas: 20 minutes
(c) fire doors in other compartment walls or floors: an equal fire resistance to the wall or floor
(d) fire doors in protecting structures above ground in flats and other residential, assembly and office occupancies: 30 minutes

(e) fire doors in other protecting structures: half the period of the fire resistance required for the wall or floor (minimum 30 minutes)
(f) any other fire doors: 20 minutes.

It should be noted that smoke control requirements are not specified for these doors.

The Home Office Guide for existing places of work that require a fire certificate generally accords with the recommendations of BS 5588, but is not specific regarding the smoke resistance of fire doors. Doors that would be deemed to be fire resisting under previous test standards are accepted, provided the premises were brought into use as a factory, office, shop or railway premises when the test was current, or the door was manufactured when the test was current. Cross-corridor doors that are intended to have only a smoke control function are not required to be fire resisting, providing they are substantial and fitted with smoke seals.

In order to serve its function, any fire door must be closed at the time of a fire. The doors should, therefore, be effectively self closing or, in the case of, for example, doors to cupboards and service shafts, be kept locked shut. Rising butt hinges are not generally acceptable as self closing devices. The self closing device should be capable of closing the door from any angle and should be capable of overcoming the resistance of any latch on the door. (Self closing devices with a "snap action" in the final part of the travel of the door can be used to ensure compliance with the latter requirement.)

If doors are a major hindrance to the flow of people or goods, they may be held open by either:

(a) A fusible link, which melts at a pre-determined temperature and causes the door to close, usually under the action of a falling weight.
(b) An electromagnetic or electro-mechanical device that permits the door to close under the action of the self closing device when smoke is detected by an automatic fire detector. Normally this arrangement comprises a continuously energised electromagnet that holds the door open by means of a metal pad on the door; the electromagnet is then de-energised when adjacent smoke detectors, or an integral smoke detector, operates. In this case, it is important that the electromagnet and the self closing device are in the same horizontal plane to prevent twisting forces that will warp the door.

It should be noted that a fusible link will not operate sufficiently early to prevent the passage of large volumes of smoke. Accordingly, this arrangement is not suitable for doors that are required to protect escape routes or equipment and stock that is sensitive to smoke damage.

Many fire authorities will not permit the use of any form of hold-open device on doors to protected staircases, and the Home Office Guide for places of work that require a fire certificate advocates against the practice. This conflicts, however, with BS 5588 Parts 2 and 3, which permit the use of suitably designed automatic release arrangements, except in the case of doors to fire fighting staircases and fire fighting lobbies (see Chapter 14) and doors to the only protected staircase that serves a building or part of a building. Insurers generally require that fire break doors are kept closed outside normal working hours. Some enforcing authorities also require that all fire resisting doors are closed at night in premises where people sleep.

Great care should be taken in the specification and fitting of hardware for fire resisting doors. Inappropriate, or inappropriately fitted, ironmongery can severely impair the fire resistance of the door. It is necessary to ensure that the melting point of any metal used in the construction of a hinge for a fire resisting door is at least 800°C. Steel hinges are ideal, but aluminium hinges and some types of brass hinge, are unsuitable. All fire resisting doors should be hung on at least three hinges, unless there is test evidence to indicate that a single pair of hinges may be used.

The fitting of locks, self closing devices and other ironmongery may result in removal of sufficient wood from the door to reduce the fire resistance to an unacceptable degree. Over-mortising is one example, since the thickness of timber that remains may be totally inadequate. The use of intumescent materials can however, help to minimise the effects of mortising. Useful guidance on ironmongery for timber fire resisting doors sets is contained in Reference 8.

Fire doors are probably the greatest potential point of weakness in a fire resisting barrier. It is, therefore, important that they are checked regularly to ensure that:

(a) no doors are wedged open
(b) the doors are not damaged, and no voids or holes have been created by removal or change of hardware

(c) the self closing devices close the door effectively, even in the case of latched doors
(d) hinges are not worn
(e) the doors remain of good fit (eg there are no gaps of more than four millimetres between the door and frame or between the leaves of double doors)
(f) intumescent seals and smoke seals are undamaged
(g) any automatic release mechanisms operate correctly
(h) no storage or rubbish will impede the effective closing of a door or shutter that is normally held open.

Glazing

Fire resisting barriers, such as walls and doors, may be glazed, provided the glazing does not reduce the overall fire resistance of the barrier. Normal glass offers no resistance to fire as it shatters and falls out at an early stage. However, various types of fire resisting glass and glazing systems are available—the most common and cheapest is fire resisting Georgian wired glass.

In more recent years, a number of unwired glasses, capable of affording substantial periods of fire resistance if installed in suitable frames and channels, have become available. They tend to be much more expensive than traditional wired glasses, but have aesthetic advantages since they are virtually indistinguishable from normal glass.

A number of proprietary glasses are also able to provide insulation. These glasses are generally laminated, with protective intumescent interlayers, which provide the insulation in the event of fire, or are sealed units that contain a heat absorbing gel. There products are, therefore, relatively thick compared with uninsulated products.

Protection Against Flame Spread over Linings

The performance requirement contained in B2 of Schedule 1 to the Building Regulations is that:

> In order to inhibit the spread of fire within the building, the surfaces of materials used on walls and ceilings:

(a) shall offer adequate resistance to the spread of flame over their surfaces; and
(b) shall have, if ignited, a rate of heat release which is reasonable in the circumstances.

Compliance with the performance requirement in practice is related to the performance of linings when tested in accordance with particular parts of BS 476 (Fire tests on building materials and structures). Part 7 of the standard (Method for classification of the surface spread of flame of products) permits materials to be grouped into four classes, according to the rate at which, in the test, flame travels over the surface of a specimen of the material. Class 1 constitutes the best performance, while Class 4 is the worst. For most commercial premises, Approved Document B permits Class 3 linings in very small rooms, but generally specifies Class 1 linings in other rooms, although small areas of Class 3 are acceptable.

In the case of circulation spaces and protected shafts, however, Approved Document B specifies on even higher requirement for linings, namely Class 0. Class 0 is a composite classification that only exists within the Building Regulations. A Class 0 material is defined as one that achieves Class 1 when tested in accordance with BS 476 Part 7, but which, in addition, will not release heat at a significant rate when the material is burning. The method by which the heat release limitation is specified in Approved Document B is complicated, and relates to further parts of BS 476. The Home Office Guides generally adopt similar principles to the Building Regulations, and each Guide contains examples of common materials with an indication of the locations in which they may be used.

Common Class 0 materials include plasterboard and mineral fibre tiles, as well as inorganic, non-combustible materials, such as brickwork, blockwork, concrete, etc. Timber is generally a Class 3 material. However, by means of treatment with fire retardant paints or intumescent coatings, the rating of timber can be improved to Class 1 or even Class 0.

Protection Against Fire Spread Beyond the Building

There are three relevant performance requirements in Part B of Schedule 1 to the Building Regulations to protect against fire spread beyond the building:

(a) A wall common to two or more buildings shall offer adequate resistance to the spread of fire and smoke.
(b) The external walls of the building shall offer adequate resistance to the spread of fire over the walls and from one building to another, having regard to the height, use of and position of the building.
(c) The roof of the building shall offer adequate resistance to the spread of fire over the roof and from one building to another, having regard to the use and position of the building.

The first of these requirements gives rise to the term *separating wall*, which is merely the fire resisting wall that separates adjoining buildings.

The second requirement gives rise to requirements for external walls to be fire resisting but, in addition, Approved Document B contains a number of additional, more detailed requirements for external walls. The Approved Document also sets out requirements for separation between buildings.

Finally, the third requirement gives rise to quite detailed requirements in Approved Document B, which relate to the performance of the roof construction in the tests contained in BS 476 Part 3: 1958 (External fire exposure roof test); this standard was, in fact, revised in 1975, but the Approved Document refers to the earlier version. The standard tests the ability of the roof to resist penetration by fire when its external surface is exposed to radiation and flame. The time to ignition and the spread of flame are measured and, in the 1958 standard, roofs are classified by two letters, "AA" being the designation for the best performance and "DD" the worst. The Approved Document relates the designation of the roof to the maximum distance of the roof from any point on the building's boundary, the purpose being to obviate fire spread to the building by radiation or flying brands from another building.

Further Reading

1. *BS 5268 Part 4 Structural use of timber*. Fire resistance of timber structures.
   Section 4.1: Recommendations for calculating fire resistance of timber members.

Section 4.2: Recommendations for calculating fire resistance of timber stud walls and joisted floor constructions.

2. *BS 5950 Part 8 Structural use of steelwork in buildings.* Code of practice for fire resistant design.
3. *BS 8110 Part 2 Structural use of concrete.* Code of practice for special circumstances.
4. Department of the Environment. *The Building Regulations 1985* Approved Document B. HMSO
5. *Rules for the Construction of Buildings Grades I and II.* Loss Prevention Council.
6. PD 6512: *Use of elements of structural fire protection with particular reference to the recommendations given in BS 5588 (Fire precautions in the design and construction of buildings)*
   Part 1: Guide to fire doors
   Part 3: Guide to the fire performance of glass.
   British Standards Institution
7. *PD 6520 Guide to fire test methods for building materials and elements of construction.* British Standards Institution.
8. *Architectural Ironmongery suitable for use on fire resisting self closing timber and emergency exit doors.* Guild of Architectural Ironmongers.
9. *Digest 208 Increasing the fire resistance of existing timber floors.* Building Research Establishment.
10. *Rules for the construction and installation of fire break doors and shutters.* Loss Prevention Council.
11. Morris W A, Read R E H and Cook G M E *Guidelines for the construction of fire resisting structural elements.* Building Research Establishment.
12. Read R E H and Morris W A *Aspects of Fire Precautions in Buildings.* HMSO
13. *Technology of fire resisting doorsets.* Timber Research and Development Association.
14. Various data sheets produced by the Fire Protection Association are also relevant to this chapter.

Chapter 8
Emergency Lighting

Types of Emergency Lighting

Emergency lighting is installed in a building to provide a degree of illumination when the normal lighting fails. The term includes:

(a) *escape lighting*, which is provided to illuminate escape routes to an extent sufficient for occupants to evacuate the building in safety
(b) *safety lighting*, which provides illumination to obviate danger to occupants, such as those engaged in a hazardous activity, due to failure of the normal lighting
(c) *standby lighting*, which is sufficient to permit normal activities in the building to continue when the general lighting fails.

Most lighting failures arise from electrical faults or complete failure of the supply from the electricity supply authority. Fire can also lead to a failure of all or part of the normal lighting, due to the effect of heat on the lighting circuits. Unless the cables are designed to be fire resisting, or are suitably protected against the fire, the cable insulation can melt, resulting in a short circuit and isolation of the circuit by the appropriate protective device (fuse or miniature circuit breaker). The failure of the normal lighting can make use of escape routes very difficult.

Fire safety only necessitates the provision of escape lighting. The term emergency lighting is commonly used to refer to what would more properly be described as escape lighting, and it is purely with escape lighting that this chapter is concerned. An element of safety lighting may, however, be incorporated in an escape lighting scheme, and will, by definition, form part of any standby lighting scheme. If standby lighting is provided in a building, it may contribute to, or constitute, the escape lighting, providing the standby lighting on escape routes complies with the requirements for escape lighting.

Need for Escape Lighting

Escape lighting is one of the supporting provisions for means of escape, and may be required under the powers of most fire safety legislation that applies to occupied buildings including, for example, the Fire Precautions Act 1971, the Housing Act 1985, and regulations that apply to places of public entertainment (see Chapter 1).

In premises where people sleep or the public assemble, escape lighting is an essential component of the fire protection measures required for safety of occupants in the event of fire. It is invariably a requirement of the relevant enforcing authority. In premises such as offices, factories and warehouses, escape lighting should certainly be provided if the premises are occupied during the hours of darkness, or if parts of the escape route are devoid of natural lighting.

If these places of work require a fire certificate it is usual for the fire authority to require escape lighting. In offices that are occupied only during normal office hours, the requirements of the fire authority in relation to the extent of escape lighting are not usually very onerous. If a fire certificate is not required for such premises, the escape lighting might not be required unless the escape routes are devoid of natural or borrowed light. Nevertheless, the provision of escape lighting should be regarded as good practice in most premises, regardless of whether it is specifically required by legislation.

Design Standards

The generally accepted design code for escape lighting is BS 5266 Part 1: 1988 (Emergency lighting. Code of practice for the emergency lighting of premises other than cinemas and certain other specified premises used for entertainment). The code is not intended to apply to ballrooms, dance halls, cinemas, bingo halls, bowling halls and similar premises. Such premises will be covered by BS 5266 Part 2, which will substantially revise BS CP 1007 (Maintained lighting for cinemas).

The Industry Committee for Emergency Lighting (ICEL) produce a very useful, detailed guide on emergency lighting. In addition, the Chartered Institute of Building Service Engineers (CIBSE) produce a technical memorandum on the subject, and this also provides guidance beyond that contained in the British Standard.

Requirements issued by enforcing authorities usually specify that any escape lighting must comply with BS 5266 Part 1 for premises to which this code applies. However, as indicated earlier, in low risk premises, such as offices, some factories and warehouses, the enforcing authority may accept escape lighting that does not comply in full with the requirements of the code in respect of, for example, area of coverage. In licensed premises, some enforcing authorities impose requirements beyond those of the code. It is important, therefore, that the relevant enforcing authority is consulted at an early stage in the specification and design of an escape lighting installation.

Choice of Installation

There are three main types of escape lighting installation:

(a) self contained luminaires
(b) central battery systems
(c) emergency generators.

Self Contained Luminaires

Escape lighting is most commonly provided by the installation of self contained luminaires, particularly in smaller premises and those premises to which escape lighting must be retrofitted. As the name implies, each luminaire is entirely independent and comprises a battery, charger, changeover device, inverter (for fluorescent fittings) and lamp(s)—all within a single housing (although the control gear may be separated from the actual lamp housing by up to one metre). It is possible to modify normal mains luminaires into self contained fittings by the addition of a conversion pack. This normally operates a small lamp within the main luminaire but, in the case of more sophisticated units, provides power to the existing lamp.

The self contained luminaire is connected to the local lighting circuit. The battery therefore remains charged by the normal lighting circuit. Failure of the normal lighting circuit is detected automatically, and illumination is provided by the emergency lighting unit.

Self contained luminaires are simple to connect and relatively cheap and quick to install, making them ideal for retrofitting into a building that has no emergency lighting. They also provide a good degree of flexibility and can be adapted to suit changes in the layout of a building. The connection to the lighting circuit may comprise any suitable cable, such as the PVC insulated and sheathed cables that are commonly used for lighting circuits. It is important, however, that they are connected to the normal lighting sub-circuit that serves the area in which they are installed; otherwise, a failure of the local lighting circuit will not be detected, and a fire that affects only this circuit will result in total loss of illumination.

A further advantage claimed for self contained luminaires is that the batteries are maintenance free, since sealed cells are used. While it is true that maintenance of batteries is not required, many users fail to appreciate that the life of these batteries is finite, and may be no more than 4–5 years. There is a tendency for the units to be installed and forgotten, with the result that, on demand, the units either fail to operate, or provide illumination for only a limited duration.

Regular testing is therefore necessary, and this may become a burden if the building is large and the number of luminaires is great. The replacement of batteries may also result in significant costs, which may ultimately exceed the economy achieved at the installation stage. Battery life will be shortened further if the units are installed in areas where the ambient temperature is high; the reliability of the associated electronics will also be affected.

Central Battery Systems

A central battery system comprises a single battery installation with associated charger. This provides a source of supply at a suitable voltage to all "slave" emergency lighting luminaires, by means of a dedicated wiring system, thus forming a complete secondary lighting installation. The batteries and control equipment are housed in a metal "cubicle", or a dedicated battery room in the case of very large sites. In order to operate fluorescent fittings, a bulk inverter is required, or alternatively, an inverter must be fitted to each luminaire. In principle, an Uninterruptible Power

Supply may be used and conventional 240V luminaires can be used as slave fittings.

Central battery systems are relatively expensive to install because of the long runs of wiring between the central point(s) and the luminaires. Further costs arise from the need to ensure that fire cannot cause loss of power to luminaires in the same way as it can affect normal lighting circuits. The wiring used must either be inherently fire resistant (eg mineral insulated copper sheathed cable), or be protected against fire by fire resisting construction; metal or rigid PVC conduit does not, by itself, provide adequate fire protection for non-fire resisting cables. Unless the protection is adequate, the entire emergency lighting installation may be vulnerable to complete failure.

Additional complexity and cost may arise from the need for sub-circuit monitoring. Unless the emergency lighting is illuminated at all times, monitoring relays in normal lighting sub-circuits will need to be installed, to ensure that failures are detected and the escape lighting is switched on.

There are, however, certain advantages in the use of central battery installations, particularly in the case of large installations with many luminaires. If vented cells are used, relatively long battery life (eg 25 years) is possible. Although these batteries will require maintenance, battery testing is simplified by the presence of a single installation. Thus, central battery systems can be cost effective for large installations.

Emergency Generators

The existence of an emergency generator may allow standby lighting to be used, but it is not necessarily adequate for escape lighting. The generator will only start on total power failure. This is not the most likely result of fire, which is more likely to affect only a limited number of circuits. Unless the generator supplies dedicated luminaires that are wired in fire resisting cable, it is unlikely to be adequate for the provision of escape lighting.

If an emergency generator is used, it must satisfy the requirement of BS 5266 Part 1 for escape lighting to be operated within 5 seconds of a mains failure (or 15 seconds in certain premises in which persons are familiar with the building, if this is acceptable to the enforcing authority). If the run-up time of the generator cannot satisfy this requirement, a back up battery with the capacity to supply emergency lighting for one hour will be required.

Mode of Operation

There are three possible modes of operation of luminaires:

(a) *non-maintained*—the luminaire operates only when the normal lighting fails
(b) *maintained*—the luminaire is illuminated at all times
(c) *sustained*—one lamp in the luminaire is energised from the emergency supply only on failure of the normal supply; the other(s) is energised from the normal mains supply.

Illuminated exit signs are often of the maintained or sustained type. Maintained emergency lighting is normally provided in theatres, concert halls, discotheques and other places of public entertainment. BS 5266 Part 1 also recommends that maintained emergency lighting be installed in escape routes within enclosed shopping malls.

Duration of Escape Lighting

BS 5266 Part 1 advocates an escape lighting duration of one hour, two hours or three hours according to the occupancy. Three hours is normally required for premises in which people sleep. Two hours is recommended for recreational premises, although one hour is considered acceptable for small premises in this class. In offices, shops and many factories, a period of one hour is usually acceptable. In practice, many manufacturers of self contained units produce only one hour and three hour units. Moreover, a number of users tend to install three hour units even where one hour units would, in theory, be acceptable.

Siting of Luminaires

A system of escape lighting should provide illumination of the following:

(a) escape routes and staircases
(b) exits (there may also be a need for external illumination unless public lighting is adequate)
(c) changes in level or direction, and intersections of corridors
(d) fire equipment (manual call points, fire extinguishers, hose reels, etc)
(e) fire safety signs (fire exit signs may be internally illuminated and form part of the escape lighting installation)
(f) large toilets
(g) plant rooms associated with normal and emergency lighting.

Although not strictly part of the escape lighting system, it is also good practice to install emergency lighting, normally of the self contained type, in lift cars. This is essential if lifts are used for evacuation of the disabled (see Chapter 6). Emergency lighting is also required in firefighting lifts (see Chapter 14).

In order to prevent obscuration by smoke, luminaires should be mounted relatively low but, to prevent obscuration by persons, a minimum height of 2m above floor level is recommended by BS 5266 Part 1. Siting should also avoid excessive contrast along the escape route and prevent glare. These design considerations are particularly important if the building may be used by partially sighted people.

Level of Illumination

In areas with defined escape routes, BS 5266 Part 1 recommends that the illuminance at floor level on the centre line of the route should be at least 0.2 lux. In addition, for escape routes up to 2m wide, the code recommends that fifty per cent of the width be lit to a minimum of 0.1 lux. Wider escape routes are treated as a number of two metre wide strips. In open plan areas with undefined escape routes, the code recommends an average illuminance of one lux over the entire area.

The levels of illuminance specified above should be achieved under the most adverse circumstances, such as voltage reduction at the end of the duration, lamp ageing and dirty diffusers on luminaires. Under normal circumstances, higher levels of illumination should exist. Nevertheless, the values specified in the British Standard are quite low (0.2 lux is equivalent to full moonlight). Higher levels may be specified by the relevant enforcing authority, and may be advisable in places in which large numbers of the public assemble, particularly if alcohol is consumed. It is likely that future European standards may call for higher emergency lighting levels.

Checking Emergency Lighting

Checking emergency lighting can prove difficult unless special test facilities are incorporated in the scheme. Central battery systems offer an advantage in that the mains supply can be isolated at a single point in order to test the central battery; checking luminaires then only involves a walk round the premises to ensure that all lamps are operational and that diffusers are clean.

Self contained luminaires are often installed without any specific test facilities. It is then necessary to identify the source of supply for each luminaire and isolate the normal lighting, in order to check the luminaires. The condition of every battery can only be proved by permitting each luminaire to discharge for a period. However, special test facilities can be incorporated in the scheme. The simplest form of test facility comprises a keyswitch that isolates the supply to a group of self contained fittings. A timer can also be fitted to ensure that the supply is restored after a pre-determined period. More sophisticated test facilities, such as hand held, infra red remote controls that put a luminaire into test mode, are also available.

BS 5266 Part 1 contains recommendations for routine inspection and testing of emergency lighting. The intervals recommended are as follows:

(a) daily
(b) monthly
(c) six monthly
(d) three yearly and, in the case of self contained luminaires, annually thereafter.

The recommendations of the Code are as follows:

Daily Inspection

(a) all maintained luminaires should be operational
(b) control equipment of central battery systems or generators should indicate normal operation.
(c) any faults should be recorded in a log book, and a note made of the action taken.

Monthly

(a) all luminaires and internally illuminated exit signs should be energised by simulating a mains failure to ensure that they operate correctly. The period of simulated failure should not exceed one quarter of the rated duration of the batteries
(b) any generators should be started up by simulating a mains failure, and should be run for at least one hour
(c) if an emergency generator has a back up battery, the generator should be prevented from starting. Mains failure should be simulated to check that the change over to the battery functions correctly; the test in (b) above should then be undertaken.

Six Monthly

(a) as well as the normal monthly test, the state of self contained batteries and central batteries should be checked by energising the luminaires for a period of one hour for batteries with a capacity of three hours, or for a period of 15 minutes if the system batteries are rated for a duration of one hour
(b) any generators with back up batteries should be prevented from starting, and mains failure should be simulated to check that the back up battery can supply the emergency lighting load for one hour. The normal monthly check of the generator should then be carried out.

Three Yearly

(a) the entire installation should be checked to ensure compliance with the design code

(b) self contained batteries and central batteries should be checked by testing the luminaires for their full rated duration
(c) any generator back up batteries should be tested for their full duration.

Subsequent Annual Test

After the first three yearly test, self contained luminaires should undergo the three yearly test on an annual basis to prove the batteries.

Further Reading

1. *BS 5266 Part 1: Emergency lighting*. Code of practice for the emergency lighting of premises other than cinemas and certain other specified premises used for entertainment.
2. *Emergency Lighting (Technical Memorandum TM12)*. Chartered Institute of Building Services Engineers.
3. *Emergency Lighting Applications Guide*. Industry Committee for Emergency Lighting.

Chapter 9

Fire Safety Signs

There are six categories of fire safety sign:

(a) safe condition
(b) mandatory
(c) fire equipment
(d) warning
(e) prohibition
(f) supplementary.

Recommendations for each type of sign are contained in BS 5499 Part 1: 1990 (Fire safety signs, notices and graphic symbols. Specification for fire safety signs). This standard is based on and refers to, BS 5378 (Safety signs and colours), and describes the colour, shape and other characteristics for each category of sign.

Many of the signs specified in BS 5499 Part 1 take the form of graphic symbols, but these may be supplemented with "supplementary" signs that bear words. (The fire exit graphic *must* for the moment, be supported by a supplementary sign.) However, to comply with the British Standard, supplementary signs can be used only with an accompanying graphic symbol. Accordingly, except where no suitable graphic symbol exists to convey the meaning required, signs complying with BS 5499 Part 1 comprise a graphic symbol, with or without an accompanying worded sign.

Table 8 contains a description of the shape, colouring and format of the five categories of sign. The size of the sign's wording or symbols depends on the distance from which the sign will be viewed. The British Standard contains guidance on letter size as a function of viewing distance.

CATEGORY OF SIGN	SHAPE	COLOURS
SAFE CONDITION	Square or oblong	White symbol or text on a green background
MANDATORY	Circular	White symbol or text on a blue background
FIRE EQUIPMENT	Square or oblong	White symbol or text on a red background
WARNING	Triangular	Black symbol or text on a yellow background surrounded by a black triangular band
PROHIBITION	Circular with cross band	Black symbol on a white background, inside a red circle with a red cross bar
SUPPLEMENTARY	Square or oblong	Black text on white background or the safety colour of the safety sign that is supplemented, with the text in the relevant contrasting colour

Table 8: Categories of fire safety sign

Fire safety signs may be self luminous or internally illuminated, but the recommendations of BS 5499 Part 1, in terms of image and graphics, remain applicable. However, constructional requirements for self luminous signs are contained in Part 2 of BS 5499, while constructional requirements for internally illuminated signs are contained in Part 3 of the standard.

Safe condition signs

The most important safe condition sign, and indeed arguably the most important of all fire safety signs, is that indicating a fire exit or the route to a fire exit. The internationally agreed symbol, now adopted by BS 5499 Part 1, is the "running man" (see Figures 24 and 25). The figure is normally running to the right (Figure 24), except in the case of an escape route that changes direction to the left, in which case Figure 25 would be used in conjunction with an arrow. In the case of a change of direction to the right, an arrow would also be used in conjunction with Figure 24.

For a transitional period, the fire exit sign will be used in the United Kingdom in conjunction with a supplementary sign bearing the words "Exit", "Fire Exit" or "Exit for emergency use only", as appropriate. As already indicated, however, these worded signs should not now be used without the accompanying graphic symbol.

Standard graphic symbols should also be used to convey the following meanings, but may, again, be supported by supplementary signs, worded as shown below:

(a) "slide to open"
(b) "break glass (or cover) in the event of fire".

The remaining standard safe condition sign contained in BS 5499 Part 1 is that used to provide instructions for panic bolts or latches, and bears the words "Push bar to open". Other safe condition signs can be constructed by using the general safe condition sign (see Figure 26) in conjunction with an appropriately worded supplementary sign.

Figure 24

Figure 25
Running man (green and white)

Figure 26: Safe condition sign (green and white)

It is conventional to indicate as "Fire Exits" only those routes of travel that are not the normal exit routes from the building, which may be signposted as "Exits". If an exit cannot be seen, or the escape route is not obvious, exit symbols should be supplemented with directional arrows.

Existing exit signs will not necessarily comply with the latest standard. This does not, however, mean that they should be replaced immediately. Any new signs should comply with the new standard. In addition, where members of the public (particularly visitors to the United Kingdom) are likely to assemble in large numbers, it would seem appropriate to phase in the internationally agreed symbol within a reasonable timescale.

Mandatory Signs

Figure 27: Mandatory sign "Fire door keep shut" (blue and white)

The most common mandatory signs are those used on fire resisting doors, each of which should bear the appropriate sign. Standard wordings for mandatory signs include:

(a) "Fire door keep shut"—used on a self-closing fire door (except an automatic fire door) when not in use, see Figure 27
(b) "Fire action"—used as a heading for written fire instructions
(c) "Fire door keep locked"—used on a fire door which is not self-closing and which must be kept locked when not in use
(d) "Automatic fire door keep clear"—used on a fire door, or shutter which becomes self-closing in the event of fire
(e) "Automatic fire door keep clear. Close at night"
(f) "Secure door open when premises are occupied"—used, for example on a door or gate opening in the wrong direction for escape
(g) "Remove security fastenings when premises are occupied"
(h) "Gangway keep clear"
(i) "Fire escape keep clear"—this sign is sometimes confused with the safe condition fire exit sign but should, typically, be used outside a fire exit door that may be obstructed.

A general mandatory symbol (see Figure 28) can be used in conjunction with appropriate supplementary signs.

Figure 28: General mandatory sign (blue and white)

Fire equipment signs

This type of sign is outside the scope of BS 5378, but is included in BS 5499 Part 1. The most important are those used to indicate the location of fire extinguishing appliances and fire alarm call points. A collection of fire equipment (ie a "fire point") should be indicated by the graphic symbol shown in Figure 29, but individual graphic symbols exist to indicate the following meanings, and may be used in conjunction with supplementary signs, such as:

(a) fire alarm call point
(b) fire telephone
(c) fire hose reel
(d) fire extinguisher.

Figure 29: Collection of firefighting equipment (red and white)

In addition, standard signs, comprising a graphic symbol and words, are contained in BS 5499 Part 1 to indicate the following:

(a) the location of a foam inlet
(b) the location of a dry riser
(c) the location of a wet riser
(d) a switch for use by firefighters (eg to ground lifts)
(e) the need to operate a valve (eg before running out a hose reel)
(f) the location of plans of the premises for use by fire fighters.

In each case, the sign comprises graphic flames in conjunction with appropriate wording.

Warning Signs

A general warning sign for use in conjunction with supplementary signs is shown in Figure 30. The most common supplementary sign is that

Figure 30: General warning (yellow and black)

indicating "In case of fire avoid use of lift". Standard graphic warning signs are contained in BS 5499 Part 1 to indicate the following meanings, which may also be conveyed by a supplementary sign, worded as shown below:

(a) "Caution risk of fire, highly flammable materials"
(b) "Caution risk of fire, oxidizing materials"
(c) "Caution risk of fire, explosive material".

A further standard sign comprising the warning triangle and the words "No escape" is used on doors, or in routes, that may appear to provide a means of escape but do not in fact do so.

Prohibition Signs

The most common prohibition sign is the universally recognised "No smoking" sign. Graphic symbols also exist to indicate that:

(a) smoking or naked flames are prohibited
(b) water must not be used as an extinguishing agent.

For other forms of prohibition, the general prohibition symbol (see Figure 31) may be used in conjunction with a supplementary sign.

Figure 31: General prohibition (red and white)

Further Reading

1. *BS 5499 Part 1: Fire safety signs, notices and graphic symbols.* Specification for fire safety signs.

Chapter 10

Fire Detection and Alarm Systems

The Need for Fire Alarm Systems and Automatic Fire Detection

In all premises, there should be some means of giving a warning to all occupants in the event of fire. In a very small, single storey building, this might comprise manually operated mechanical devices, such as turn-handle rotary gongs. If the premises were small enough, it might even be sufficient for persons to shout "Fire!" in order for an adequate warning to be given. In practice, most buildings require an electrically operated fire alarm installation that will alert all occupants, indicate the location of the fire and, perhaps, automatically summon the fire brigade.

In the case of a manual system, the fire warning signal can be initiated only by the operation of a trigger device (see below) by occupants. With an automatic system, the warning can be initiated by strategically sited automatic fire detectors (see below). In practice, any automatic fire alarm system is normally combined with a manual fire alarm system.

In premises to which the Fire Precautions Act applies, the presence of a manual fire alarm system will normally be a prerequisite for certification; in the case of hotels, the system will normally be required to incorporate automatic fire detectors. Fire alarm systems can also be required under most other fire safety legislation, and automatic detection may be required, for example, in certain houses in multiple occupation under the powers granted by the Housing Acts (see Chapter 1).

An automatic fire detection system may also be regarded by enforcing authorities to compensate for deficiencies in other fire protection measures, particularly means of escape. There is some logic in this principle, since automatic fire detectors may alert occupants before they would otherwise become aware of a fire. The occupants may then begin to use the means of escape, before the shortcomings that exist cause the escape route to become impassable.

Fire insurers may also strongly encourage the installation of automatic fire detection in a building, in order to reduce the likely property damage in the event of a fire. In some premises, particularly those of an industrial nature, insurers may actually grant a small discount in fire insurance premiums if automatic fire detection of a type approved by the Loss Prevention Council (LPC) is installed throughout the premises in accordance with LPC Rules (see below).

Design Codes

In the United Kingdom, most fire alarm installations are designed in accordance with BS 5839 Part 1: 1988 (Fire detection and alarm systems for buildings. Code of practice for system design, installation and servicing). If a fire alarm system is required by an enforcing authority, they will normally require compliance with this code.

The LPC also publish *Rules for automatic fire alarm installations for the protection of property*, which are in close accordance with the recommendations of BS 5839 Part 1 for a P1 system, as defined in the code (see below), but which also require there to be means for automatic summoning of the fire brigade by methods defined in the Rules. In practice, few installations are designed to comply specifically with these Rules, and in due course it is possible that the LPC Rules will simply require compliance with the British Standard and, perhaps, some minor additional requirements.

Categories of Installation

BS 5839 Part 1 defines six categories of installation:

(a) *Type P1 systems* are intended for the protection of property, and incorporate automatic fire detection throughout the protected building.

(b) *Type P2 systems* are also installed for the protection of property, but incorporate automatic fire detection only in defined parts of the building.
(c) *Type L1 systems* are intended for the protection of life, and incorporate automatic fire detection throughout the protected building.
(d) *Type L2 systems* are also intended for the protection of life, but incorporate automatic fire detection only in defined parts of the building, which include those parts in which a type L3 system would require detectors to be installed.
(e) *Type L3 systems* are installed only for the protection of escape routes; the objective is to ensure that occupants evacuate before escape routes become too difficult to use.
(f) *Type M systems* do not incorporate automatic fire detectors; they are, by definition, manual fire alarm systems.

In addition, systems intended for installation in multi-occupancy buildings are given the suffix X. Special consideration is required for such systems, due to the absence of control by a single occupant.

In practice, Type M systems are very common. However, the sub-categories of Types P and L systems are usually found only in combination with Type M systems. Exceptions do, however, exist; for example, in a building that is protected throughout by a simple Type M system, a Type P2 system may be installed quite independently to protect a computer suite.

The distinction between property protection and life safety may, at first sight, seem somewhat academic; any system that satisfies one objective will, to a greater or lesser extent, satisfy the other. Certainly, it is true that there is, for example, a great deal of similarity between a Type P1 and a Type L1 installation. Nevertheless, subtle differences in, for example, the spacing between detectors in staircases and corridors may arise according to whether a life safety or a property protection objective applies. Accordingly, in purchasing specifications, it is very important to define clearly the category of system that is required.

As already indicated, an installation that complies with the LPC Rules is, effectively, a P1 installation in terms of the British Standard. However, the Rules divide installations into 3 categories, defined as Class A, Class B and Class C, according to whether the maximum attendance time of the fire brigade is respectively 5 minutes, 10 minutes or 15 minutes. It is likely that, if an insurance premium discount is granted, the discount would be highest for a Class A installation and lowest for a Class C installation.

Components of an Installation

A schematic of a typical fire alarm installation is shown in Figure 32. The basic components of an installation are as follows:

(a) trigger devices/sensors—manual fire alarm call points and automatic fire detectors
(b) control and indicating equipment (with associated power supplies)
(c) alarm devices—bells, electronic sounders, etc
(d) wiring (but interconnection may instead be by radio signalling).

To these basic components, may be added optional extras, such as:

(e) a remote centre transmitter that will transmit any alarm to a remote location
(f) interfaces with other systems, such as air conditioning and ventilation plant, gaseous extinguishing installations, plant shutdown facilities, door release units, etc.

Manual Call Points

Manual call points are devices by which building occupants can raise the alarm of fire. They comprise a frangible element, such as a piece of glass, which breaks, or appears to break, on operation of the device. The operation of the device must require only a single action, which should be irreversible by the operator.

They should be sited on exit routes, on staircase landings and at final exits. No person should need to travel more than 30m from any point in a building to reach the nearest manual call point. It is also good practice to site manual call points at zone junctions (see below) and near specific hazards, such as paint spray booths.

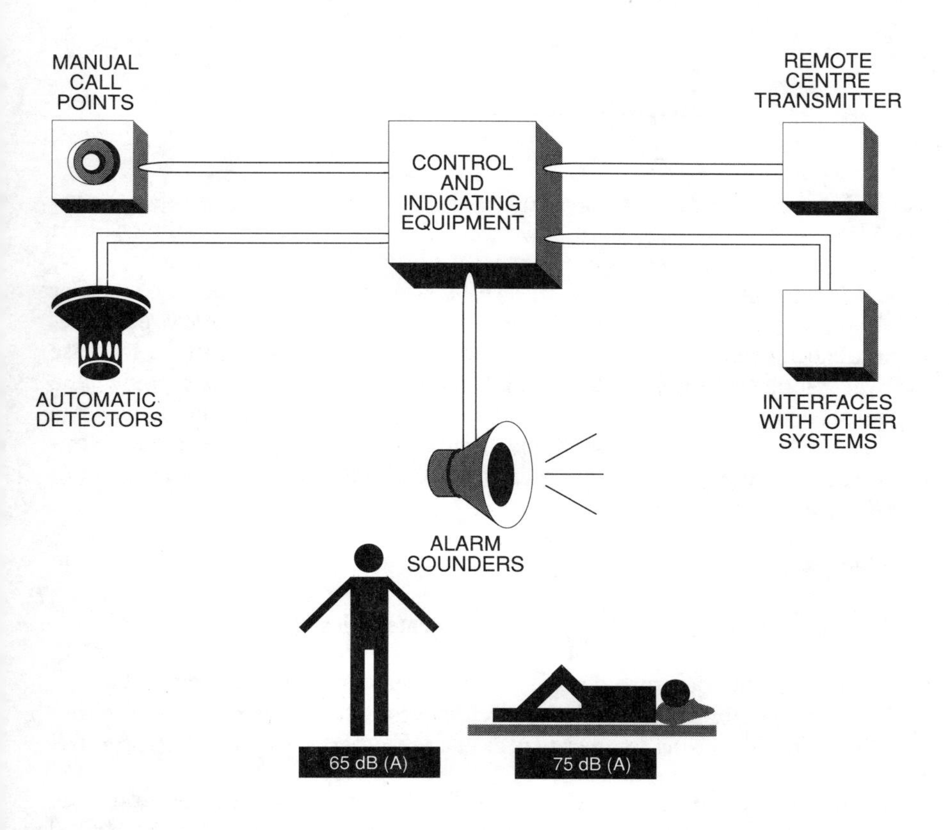

Figure 32: Schematic of typical fire alarm installation

Automatic fire detectors

Automatic fire detectors respond to one or more of the three characteristic products of fire:

(a) heat
(b) smoke
(c) flame.

These products may be sensed at either a single point within the volume of the protected space by a *point detector*, or along a defined line within the space by a *line detector*.

Line detectors may be *integrating* or *non-integrating*, according to whether they integrate the effect of the characteristic along a line. For example, integrating type line heat detectors respond to a low temperature increase over a long length, as well as a high temperature increase at a point. The non-integrating type respond only to the effect of the phenomenon at a point (eg, by detecting *only* a high temperature increase at a point). Non-integrating line detectors can, therefore, be thought of as an infinite number of point detectors.

Heat detectors

Heat detectors may be divided into two categories:

(a) fixed temperature devices, which behave rather like thermostats
(b) fixed temperature/rate of rise devices, which will respond to either a rapidly rising temperature or at a pre-determined fixed temperature.

Rate of rise detectors without a fixed temperature of operation are manufactured, but are not normally acceptable for installation in the United Kingdom.

Point heat detectors may be electromechanical in nature (eg comprise bi-metallic strips), but modern devices are normally either pneumatic or, more commonly, electronic (eg thermistor based) in nature. Line-type heat detectors may be based on pneumatic or, more commonly, electrical principles. Non-integrating line heat detectors usually comprise a length of current-carrying cable, in which the insulation melts at a defined temperature, resulting in a short circuit. In integrating line heat detecting cables, the capacitance and/or resistance of the insulation changes with temperature.

Heat detectors may be used for general property protection, but will normally be much slower to operate than smoke detectors. Flames could be as much as one-third of the way to the ceiling before a heat detector will operate. As the ceiling height increases, the fire size at the point of detection increases dramatically. If the ceiling height is doubled, for example, the size of the fire at the point of detection is likely to increase by a factor of five to six. The response of heat detectors is too slow to be of use in escape routes or in areas, such as computer suites, where a small fire could cause a significant loss.

Heat detectors are necessary, however, in areas in which dust, fumes, etc may preclude the use of smoke detectors (eg kitchens). They may also be used in areas in which a fire is likely to produce a high heat output rather than smoke (eg certain flammable liquids risks). Heat detectors may also be suitable for installation in rooms enclosed in fire resisting construction, if the fire protection objective is simply to provide warning before the integrity of the construction is threatened. A particular example of this is rooms adjoining escape routes where, to satisfy the life safety objective, it may only be necessary to provide early warning before a fire resisting door fails to hold back fire and smoke.

Normally, any heat detectors used are of the fixed temperature/rate of rise, point type. However, fixed temperature detectors should be used where sudden rises in ambient temperature may occur (eg, near ovens or in laundry rooms). Line heat detectors tend to be used for special applications, where the geometry of the protected space is particularly conducive to their use (eg cable tunnels and under escalators).

Smoke detectors

There are two types of point smoke detector, namely:

(a) the ionisation chamber smoke detector
(b) the optical scattering smoke detector.

Ionisation chamber detectors contain a radioactive source, which ionises the air within the chamber, so allowing a small current to pass between two electrodes. Smoke particles interfere with the ion transport and lead to ion–electron recombination, so reducing the current. The reduction in current is sensed as an alarm condition.

Optical detectors contain a light emitting diode and a receiver. The detection principle is usually based on light scattering—the effect of smoke is to scatter light from the transmitter towards the receiver. However, in principle, obscuration of light by smoke could be used as in the case of beam detectors (see below).

Line type smoke detectors use a beam of light (often in the infra red part of the spectrum). A transmitter and receiver unit are mounted on opposing walls which, typically may be up to 100m apart. In some systems, normally used for relatively small areas, the transmitter and receiver may be housed in a single unit, and the beam is reflected off a relatively small passive reflector. Some types of beam detector are also designed to respond to thermal turbulence, which, in effect, makes these detectors combined heat and smoke detectors.

Smoke detectors are quite sensitive, which means that they are faster in response than heat detectors but much more susceptible to false alarms. There is overlap in the range of particle sizes to which optical and ionisation chamber detectors are sensitive; this means that either type is suitable for general applications. However, ionisation chamber detectors are sensitive to the very small invisible particles that are produced in rapid flaming and clean burning fires; optical detectors are less sensitive to these small particles, but are more sensitive than ionisation chamber detectors to the larger particles that occur in the cooler products of slow smouldering or in smoke that has "aged". Optical detectors are more likely to produce false alarms from tobacco smoke, whereas ionisation chamber detectors sometimes result in false alarms due to fumes from cooking processes, eg burnt toast. Ionisation chamber detectors may also false alarm if installed in high air flows.

There is a general tendency to use smoke detectors for general property protection, except in areas where processes or environmental influences may cause false alarms. Ionisation chamber detectors are probably the more common type of detector in this case, but optical detectors should be considered where slow smouldering fires might occur, as in the case of rooms housing large quantities of electric cables.

Smoke detectors are also generally used for life safety applications. Conventionally, optical smoke detectors are installed in escape routes, while ionisation (or optical) detectors are installed in other areas.

Beam detectors may prove economical for protection of large, open areas, such as warehouses, provided the transmitter and receiver can be firmly attached to solid construction, and the beam will not be obscured by, for example, fork lift trucks. Beam detectors may also be useful in situations in which a ceiling mounted detector may be unacceptable, eg historic buildings.

Aspirating smoke detection systems

In these systems, a pump or fan draws air samples from the protected space (through holes in small bore tubing or pipework within the protected space) to a central smoke detector. The detector used may be of the ionisation chamber or optical type and is normally extremely sensitive. These systems are increasingly used for the protection of computer rooms, in which it is quite common to use them for monitoring return air to air conditioning units.

At present, there are no British Standards for the equipment or codes for their application. This makes the user very dependent on the expertise of the installer.

Flame detectors

Flame detectors either detect the infra red or ultra violet radiation that is emitted from flame. Infra red detectors use a solid state infra red sensor, while ultra violet detectors are usually similar in principle to Geiger-Mueller tubes. In the case of infra red detectors, in order to filter out extraneous sources of infra red radiation, the detectors will give an alarm only if the radiation has the characteristic "flicker" frequency associated with fires.

Flame detectors are basically line-of-sight devices. It is necessary for them to be able to survey the entire protected area without obstruction. These detectors are expensive and the nature of their response makes them suitable mainly for special applications, such as flammable liquids plant. Ultra violet detectors tend to be used outdoors, although solar blind infra red detectors are available. Infra red detectors can also be used for indoor applications, if the ceiling height is such that the products of combustion may not rise to operate heat or smoke detectors until the fire is very large, eg a cathedral.

Control and indicating equipment

The control and indicating equipment is the "heart and brains" of a fire alarm installation. It provides power to the trigger devices and sounders, monitors the trigger devices and any interconnecting cable to trigger devices and sounders, etc. The power supplies are normally derived from the mains, but there should also be a standby supply in the form of batteries.

When a manual call point or automatic fire detector operates, the control and indicating equipment provides an indication of the area (or zone) of alarm origin. The indication may take the form of a set of lamps, or an illuminated mimic plan of the premises. Ancillary text information can also be displayed on a liquid crystal or vacuum fluorescent display, or on a visual display unit.

At the control panel, the alarm sounders may be silenced by authorised users, and the system may be reset after an alarm condition. Normally, there are also facilities to isolate zones or devices, and sometimes certain test facilities are incorporated.

The siting of the indicating equipment is important. It should be generally located so that it is readily available to the fire brigade as they enter the building. Repeater panels or mimics may be sited at several locations, so that the information is available at all strategic entrances to a complex building.

Alarm devices

Alarm signals are most commonly given by bells or electronic sounders. The decision as to which type of device to use is largely a matter of taste. Either can be used in staged alarm systems, in which the "evacuate" signal is given in the area immediately affected and an "alert" signal (eg pulsing bells) is given in other areas.

Whatever device is selected, the sound level produced at any point in a building should not be less than 65dB(A) or 5dB(A) above any background noise, whichever is greater. If there are sleeping occupants, a sound level of 75dB(A) should be provided at the bedhead.

A public address system, either dedicated to emergency situations or used for everyday purposes, may be used instead of sounders. The public address system must in this case comply with the relevant requirements of standards for fire alarm systems, which will normally necessitate special design considerations, and in the event of fire all inputs must be isolated except those required for producing the fire warning or providing supplementary information. The use of public address offers certain advantages over conventional alarm sounders, particularly in complex buildings, large public buildings, and in buildings with phased evacuation (see Chapter 6).

People respond better to voice messages than simple alarm bells. Alarm messages can be recorded and stored in solid state memories and, by using a dedicated "fire" microphone, evacuation can be controlled in a much more sophisticated manner than would be possible with a simple on/off device, such as a bell or electronic sounder.

In areas with high noise levels, visual alarms, such as flashing beacons, may be necessary to supplement the alarm sounders. These may also be of value in areas in which profoundly deaf people work, and are sometimes used in television or radio studios in which audible sounders must be isolated during live transmissions. In sleeping accommodation for deaf people, a combination of flashing beacons and vibrating pads, which are located under pillows or mattresses, may be incorporated into the fire alarm system to rouse the occupants.

Wiring

Wiring to sounders, detectors and call points must be monitored by the control equipment so that a fault warning is generated in the event of an open circuit or short circuit. It is still necessary to ensure that the cable type and/or protection is such that it is not susceptible to mechanical damage. For critical circuits that must continue to operate once fire is detected—such as circuits supplying alarm sounders—the circuit must not fail because of fire damage to the cable. This requirement does not generally apply to the circuits of trigger devices that should operate before fire damages the cable.

In practice, the most common types of cable used are:

(a) mineral insulated copper sheathed cable
(b) silicone rubber insulated cable with a PVC/aluminium composite sheath
(c) PVC insulated cable in metal or rigid PVC conduit.

The first two types of cable may be used for critical circuits without additional fire protection. (In principle, other cables that satisfy specific fire resistance requirements when tested in accordance with BS 6387 [Specification for performance requirements for cables required to maintain circuit integrity during fire conditions] may be used.) PVC insulated cables in conduit should not be used for sounder circuits without additional fire protection, eg burying in 12mm of plaster.

Only mineral insulated copper sheathed cables and steel wire armoured cables can be used absolutely in any situation without additional mechanical protection. If PVC insulated non-sheathed cables are used, they always require mechanical protection. Other cable types should be given mechanical protection if they are less than 2.25m above floor level, or if physical damage or rodent attack is likely. Mechanical protection can be afforded by conduit, ducting or trunking, or by laying the cable in a channel.

Radio-linked Systems

It is possible to link components of a fire alarm system by radio, thereby obviating the need for wiring. Radio-linked systems are sometimes regarded as an attractive solution for buildings in which wiring would be detrimental to the aesthetics of the building, and can be used to provide temporary protection that is quick to install and adaptable. However, one disadvantage with these systems, is that their trigger devices and sounders must be provided with local power. Normally, in the case of detectors and call points, this comprises an internal primary battery with a second reserve primary battery. Thus, there is a need to change batteries in all devices periodically. In the case of sounders, these are either conventionally wired, or operated by radio and powered from local mains supplies, in which case a standby battery supply is, again, required.

Types of Fire Alarm System

There are two basic types of fire alarm system, which differ according to the method by which the detectors and call points communicate with the control and indicating equipment. The two types of system may be described as:

(a) non-addressable
(b) addressable.

In a fire situation, a non-addressable system will be unable to identify at the control and indicating equipment which of the devices on the particular circuit has operated—only a zone indication can be given. In order to minimize the delay in locating the fire, BS 5839 Part 1 imposes restrictions on the size of a zone.

In an addressable system the signals from each device are individually identified at the control panel. In the event of a fire alarm signal, the exact identity (and location) of the initiating device can be shown at the control panel. Although zone indication is also given as a more coarse form of indication, zoning is not associated with circuits, but is a software function of the system, ie "addresses" are configured into zones by the system software.

Although the area of a zone remains limited by BS 5839 Part 1, a single circuit can serve many zones, and it is usually possible to connect more devices on a single pair of conductors than would be possible in a non-addressable system.

There are three categories of addressable system, according to whether the detectors are:

(a) two state
(b) multi-state
(c) analogue.

Two state detectors are no different in principle to the two state detectors in non-addressable systems but, of course, they transmit their individual identity along with the fire signal. Analogue detectors contain no circuitry to make the decision as to whether or not there is a fire—they are merely sensors that continually transmit a signal level that corresponds to the instantaneous value of the phenomenon that they are measuring, ie heat, smoke or flame. The actual decision as to whether the signal level is representative of a fire is taken at the control and indicating equipment.

In the simplest analogue systems, the control equipment indicates four states for any detector, eg Normal, Fault, Pre-Warning and Fire.

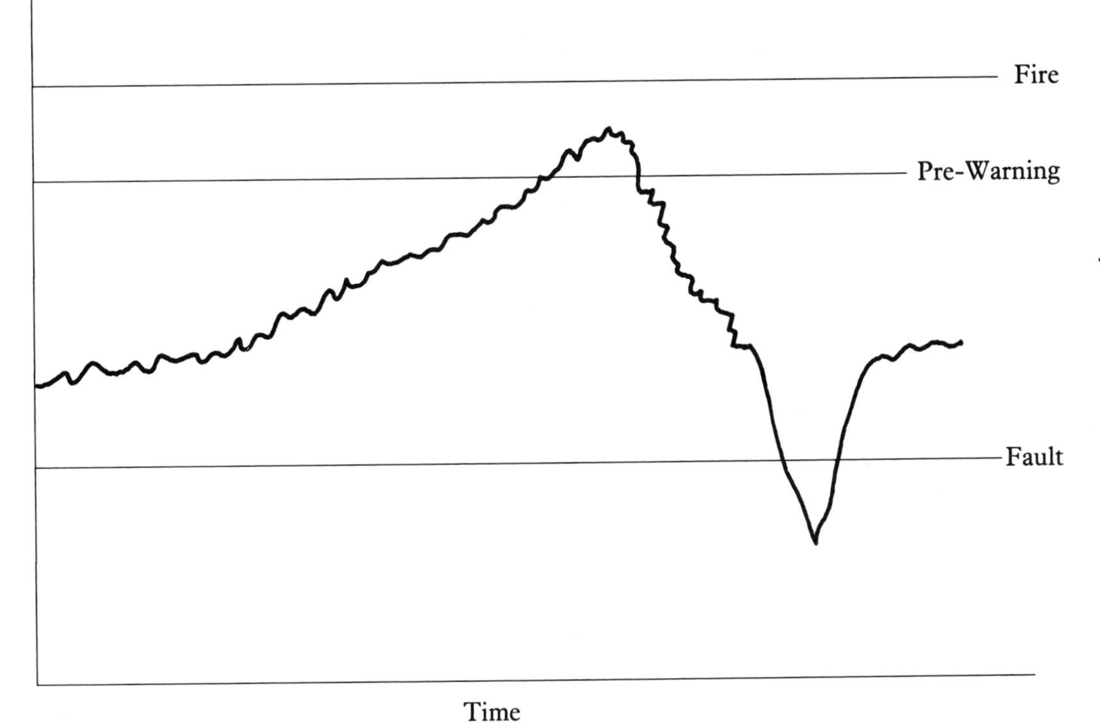

Figure 33

The fault signal would be given when the signal level became very low, indicating a lack of sensitivity, while the pre-warning would be indicative of a signal level that had risen above the normal level but had not yet reached the fire threshold (see Figure 33). In more sophisticated systems, the thresholds may be varied automatically to compensate for changes in the environment and pollution of smoke detectors.

Such is the processing power that can now be built into a small package that the application of fixed thresholds, and an element of signal processing, can be undertaken at each detector head, which then need transmit only specific conditions, such as the four states defined above. This is the manner in which a multi-state detector operates.

The function of the pre-warning state given by many analogue and multi-state systems is to obviate potential false alarms and enable early investigation of an incipient fire. Thus pre-warning signals do not result in a general alarm, but normally merely give a warning at the control and indicating equipment.

Many analogue systems offer other advantages. They enable the facility to "interrogate" each sensor at the control equipment to obtain an output of its present signal level. This can be of use to service engineers in identification of sensors that require to be cleaned. It is also, in theory, possible to vary the system performance, such as on a time-related basis, to enable higher sensitivity when the premises are unoccupied and false alarms are less likely to occur by such enhanced sensitivity.

False Alarms

False alarms remain a very significant problem for users of automatic fire detection systems, and colour the judgement of building occupants regarding the effectiveness of these systems and the significance of an alarm condition. Around 93% of calls to fire brigades as a result of fire alarm actuation are false alarms.

However, the newer generation systems, particularly those of the analogue type should perform better.

Common causes of false alarms (per BS 5839 Part 1) are:

(a) mechanical and electrical faults, often resulting from the effects of vibration, impact or corrosion

(b) ambient conditions such as heat, smoke or flame from work processes or cooking, fumes from engine exhausts or high air velocities due to strong winds
(c) work being carried out in a protected area without the necessary precautions
(d) communication faults arising from servicing or testing work carried out without prior notification of the remote manned centre, or arising from the activities of the public telecommunications operator
(e) electrical transients or radio interference
(f) inadequate servicing
(g) the build up of dust or dirt within the detector, or the entry of insects
(h) changes within the building
(i) accidental or malicious operation of call points or detectors.

In some of the above cases, the system has operated perfectly correctly within its design parameters. The fire alarm industry attempted to introduce the term "unwanted alarm" as a euphemism for these. In practice, the user is not generally concerned regarding the distinction; false alarms result in disruption, loss of profit and loss of credibility in evacuation signals.

Transmission to the Fire Brigade

In general, automatic fire detection only contributes to property protection if it causes the fire brigade to be summoned. The system will only be effective in reduction of loss if it is continuously monitored at a manned location, from where the brigade can be summoned without delay. In practice there is often a need for signals to be transmitted automatically, without manual intervention by persons at the protected premises. For an automatic fire detection system to be recognised by insurers, automatic transmission to a "remote manned centre" is a requirement, although this facility cannot be required under legislation.

In the 1970s it was commonplace for signals to be transmitted automatically to fire brigade control rooms over private wires rented from the then Post Office. Today, it is extremely rare for any fire brigade to monitor alarms. The most important exception involves a British Telecom system, known as Alarms by Carrier (ABC), in which fire alarm signals are transmitted over the subscriber's normal telephone line and routed automatically to the brigade. However, this system is available in only a limited geographical area and is unlikely to be subject to significant geographical expansion.

Alarm messages can also be transmitted automatically by means of a 999 Auto-dialler. This device automatically dials 999 and plays a taped message. Although very cheap and simple, the reliability is not high due to the electromechanical nature of the equipment and the dependence on magnetic tape. This type of system is gradually being phased out by the alarm industry.

In practice, most automatic transmission of signals involves transmission to an alarm company's *central station*, from where alarm conditions are monitored and the fire brigade are summoned. Means for automatic transmission to a central station can be divided into three categories:

(a) Digital communicators, which automatically dial up the central station and transmit a coded signal to a receiver at the central station.
(b) Dedicated circuits, established over private wires that run from the protected premises to the central station.
(c) British Telecom's "CARE" System, which is similar in principle to ABC but is used to route signals to a central station rather than the fire brigade.

Digital communicators are slower and less reliable than the other methods, and can be affected by congestion in the public switched telephone network (PSTN).

CARE is also economical because it uses an existing telephone line and cost is, therefore, independent of distance. It is, at present, only available in selected areas of the country, but is being expanded.

Dedicated circuits are connected via telephone exchanges and provide a permanent dedicated path which avoids the PSTN. There are three types of dedicated route:

(a) Direct connection from protected premises to central station.
(b) Omnibus circuit, in which that part of the path between the telephone exchange and the central station is shared by several subscribers.
(c) Connection to a "satellite" (data concentrator), either by direct connection or omnibus circuit. From the data concentrator a large

number of subscribers' signals are routed via a dedicated multiplex circuit.

Private wires are expensive. The cost of a connection is very dependent on the distance from the protected premises to the nearest central station or satellite. The use of the line sharing techniques described in (b) and notably (c), enable significant economies without significant loss of reliability.

There is currently no code of practice for the transmission of signals to the brigade. As well as the variation in reliability, cost and speed of transmission between the various methods of transmission, central station standards and operating practices vary from one central station operating company to the next. The Loss Prevention Certification Board (LPCB) do, however, operate a certification scheme for central stations, and there is an LPCB standard against which the central stations can be assessed.

Checking Fire Alarm Systems

BS 5839 Part 1 recommends that the user carry out certain checks on a daily, weekly and monthly basis, as follows:

Daily

(a) It should be ensured that the control panel indicates normal operation, or that faults are recorded and receive attention. It should also be ensured that any previously recorded fault has received attention.
(b) Any unmonitored remote link should be tested.

Weekly

(a) At least one detector, call point or end of line test switch should be operated to test the system. More than one device may need to be tested, as all zones should be tested over a period of not more than 13 weeks. Records should be kept so that devices can be tested in rotation.
(b) A visual check of accessible batteries should be made. Low electrolyte levels in vented cells should be topped up.

(c) The fuel, oil and coolant levels of any standby generator should be checked and topped up as necessary.
(d) Any printer should be checked to ensure that its reserves of paper, ink or ribbon are adequate for at least two weeks normal usage.

Monthly

If an automatic emergency generator forms part of the standby supply, it should be operated by simulation of mains failure, and allowed to run for at least one hour.

The entire installation should be subject to a quarterly inspection and test by a competent person. Except in very large organisations with in-house expertise, this will normally involve a service visit by a specialist contractor, with whom there should be a standing contract for quarterly visits and emergency maintenance.

Routine safety inspections should ensure that access to manual call points is not obstructed. A clear space around detector heads should also be maintained so that the flow of smoke and hot gases to the heads is not obstructed. The siting of call points, detectors and sounders must remain appropriate following any changes to the layout or partitioning within the building.

Further Reading

1. *BS 5839 Part 1: Fire detection and alarm systems for buildings.* Code of practice for system design, installation and servicing.
2. *Rules for automatic fire alarm installations for the protection of property.* Loss Prevention Council.
3. Burry P *Fire detection and alarm systems.* A guide to the BS Code BS 5839 Part 1. Paramount Publishing Ltd ISBN 0 947 665113.

Chapter 11

Fire Extinguishing Appliances

Fire extinguishing appliances in buildings may comprise any of the following:

(a) portable fire extinguishers
(b) trolley-mounted fire extinguishers
(c) fire blankets
(d) hydraulic hose reels.

Trolley-mounted extinguishers are used only for special applications where there may be a need for trained occupants to tackle a very large fire, such as one involving a large quantity of flammable liquids. They are, therefore, not considered further.

Need for Fire Extinguishing Appliances

Most fire safety legislation requires there to be adequate fire extinguishing appliances in any building to which the legislation is relevant. In theory, either portable fire extinguishers or hose reels may be provided. In practice, it might be appropriate to consider hose reels as supplementary to portable extinguishers, rather than as a direct alternative. Extinguishers offer the advantage that they can be used on a fire very quickly, while hose reels may take longer to run out. However, hose reels provide an unlimited supply of extinguishing agent, and thus enable a much greater degree of "first aid" fire fighting.

Fire insurers will normally require that a building is provided with fire extinguishing appliances. Discounts may apply if sufficient appliances of a suitable type are provided in accordance with insurers' rules on the subject.

There is ample evidence to demonstrate the great importance of fire fighting equipment in buildings. The significance is not apparent from

Home Office statistics on fires, as these relate only to fires to which the fire brigade were summoned. However, statistics produced by the Fire Extinguishing Trades Association (FETA) indicate that, in 1990, member companies (who are involved in the manufacture and servicing of fire extinguishing appliances) received reports of 927 fires in which fire extinguishing appliances were used. Of these, 75% were not even reported to the fire brigade, but were extinguished by occupants of the building. A number of those reported to the fire brigade were also extinguished before the arrival of the brigade. Only 11% of the reported fires were in fact extinguished by the fire brigade. Fire extinguishing appliances have, therefore, an important role to play in the fire protection of any building.

Portable Fire Extinguishers

Agents

Portable fire extinguishers may contain any one of the five recognised extinguishing agents, namely:

(a) water
(b) foam
(c) powder
(d) halon
(e) carbon dioxide.

Water

Water is the most common extinguishing agent, and is suitable for Class A risks (see Chapter 2), which involve "normal" combustibles, such as wood, paper, textiles, etc. Water is not suitable for Class B fires (involving flammable liquids, etc), nor for discharge onto live electrical equipment. Water extinguishes fire by cooling the fuel, into which the discharge from a portable extinguisher can normally penetrate reasonably well.

The most common size of extinguisher contains nine litres of water, which provides a discharge for around one minute. The throw of the discharged water is approximately six metres. The discharge results either from release of permanently stored pressure (in which case the extinguisher bears a pressure gauge), or from the generation of pressure, on operation of the appliance, due to the release of gas from an internal, pre-sealed gas cartridge.

Water extinguishers are relatively heavy (a full extinguisher typically weighs around 13kg) and some staff may find them difficult to carry.

Foam

Two types of foam may be found in portable extinguishers:

(a) fluoroprotein foam
(b) aqueous film forming foam (AFFF).

Fluoroprotein foam is intended for use on Class B fires, while AFFF may be used on Class A or Class B fires. Foam extinguishes flammable liquids fires by smothering—the foam creates a barrier between the liquid surface and the surrounding air. AFFF extinguishes Class A fires in much the same manner as water, but the reduced surface tension created by the additive aids the wetting of the fuel surface.

The size and weight of foam extinguishers are similar to those of water extinguishers, although AFFF extinguishers containing less than 9 litres of agent are available. The efficiency of the latter appliances is such that they can achieve the same Class A rating (see below) as a nine litre water extinguisher. As in the case of water extinguishers, the applicances may be either of the stored pressure or gas cartridge type.

Foam is not particularly effective on running flammable liquid fires, nor should it be used on fires involving live electrical equipment. Certain AFFF spray extinguishers are incapable of conducting an electric current down the actual discharge from the extinguisher, but the dampened surfaces on which the operators may then stand could pose a danger to operators if they came into contact with live electrical equipment.

Powder

Depending on the agent used, powder extinguishers may be suitable for both Class A and Class B fires, or only for Class B fires. Extinguishers usually contain several kilograms of agent, and the mechanism of expulsion may, again, be stored pressure or gas cartridge. The gross weight of the extinguisher is usually less than that of a water or foam extinguisher (typically 5–10kg), and the range of the discharge is around five metres. The means by which powder extinguishes fire is very complex (see Chapter 2), but involves chemical inhibition and the imposition of a thermal load.

Powder provides very rapid knockdown of flame, and the performance ratings achieved for both Class A and Class B fires are quite high. Powders are also quite effective on running flammable liquid fires. A disadvantage of powder, however, is that it has no cooling effect and cannot readily prevent re-ignition of a fire that continues to smoulder after the extinguisher is discharged. Powder may be used on live electrical equipment, but may cause significant damage to electronic and electromechanical equipment.

Halon

Halon extinguishers contain an agent known as halon 1211 or bromochlorodifluoromethane (BCF). The extinguishers normally contain 1.5–3.5kg of agent, although larger extinguishers are also produced. Thus, the weight of the extinguisher is relatively low (eg five kilograms). Halon is a vaporising liquid—stored as a liquid under pressure but evaporating rapidly on discharge. Because the initial throw is in the form of a liquid, the range is good (eg five metres), but the discharge time is quite short (10–15 seconds). The means by which halon extinguishes flame is complex, but basically it interferes with the chemical reaction that occurs in flame.

Halon is a useful agent as it is "clean", leaving no residues, and can be used on live electrical equipment. It is also suitable for use on Class B and small Class A fires, which it will knock down quite quickly. Unfortunately, halons deplete the ozone layer and, under the terms of the Montreal Protocol on Substances that Deplete the Ozone Layer (an international agreement), production will be phased out by the end of the century, except for a very limited number of essential uses. In the meantime, most responsible organisations attempt to avoid the use of halon unless there is no suitable alternative.

The toxicity of halon is low and, in the quantities used in extinguishers, it is safe to discharge in general areas of a building. However, it should not be discharged in a very confined space.

Carbon Dioxide

Carbon dioxide extinguishes fire by displacing oxygen and imposing a thermal load on the flames. Most portable extinguishers contain either around two or five kilograms of the agent but, as the gas is stored as a liquid under high pressure, the cylinder itself is heavy, and the typical gross weights of extinguishers are in the region of 5–12kg. The extinguishing performance is, however, significantly less than that of other extinguishers of similar weight, and CO_2 extinguishers are provided mainly for use on fires involving electrical equipment. In office areas, it is common to provide CO_2 extinguishers, in conjunction with water or AFFF extinguishers, purely for use on electrical equipment as, like halon, the gas leaves no residues.

Carbon dioxide extinguishers should not be discharged into confined spaces as the gas is both an asphyxiant and toxic. In the quantities used in portable extinguishers, however, there is no significant danger from using carbon dioxide in normal areas of commercial and industrial buildings.

Carbon dioxide extinguishers are not particularly "user-friendly", in that their weight is high in relation to their extinguishing capability and they generate a significant amount of noise when they are operated. Also, the discharge horn becomes very cold during the discharge and, if gripped tightly for long periods, mild frostbite can result. However, since they do not contribue to depletion of the ozone layer, they are preferable to halon extinguishers for small fires involving electrical equipment, but it is essential that staff are aware of the noise that will be created and the correct method of holding the extinguisher.

Relevant Standards

The manufacturing standard for portable fire extinguishers is BS 5423 (Specification for portable fire extinguishers). Extinguishers manufactured in accordance with the standard have a controllable discharge facility, so that it is not necessary to discharge the entire contents of the appliance. Guidance on siting of fire extinguishers is contained in BS 5306 Part 3 (Fire extinguishing installations and equipment on premises. Code of practice for selection, installation and maintenance of portable fire extinguishers).

The Loss Prevention Council (LPC) and the British Approvals for Fire Equipment (BAFE) both publish lists of extinguishers that have been independently tested in accordance with BS 5423, and that are manufactured in accordance with a satisfactory quality assurance scheme. Specification of such independently certificated extinguishers provides an assurance of product quality and reliability.

Siting of Extinguishers

Extinguishers should be sited in conspicuous locations on escape routes, such as at storey exits and in corridors, and should be wall mounted on brackets. No person should need to travel further than 30m to reach the nearest extinguisher. It may also be advisable to provide additional extinguishers of a suitable type in close proximity to particular hazards. For example, a CO_2 or halon extinguisher is normally provided in the vicinity of any large photocopying machine.

Extinguishers complying with BS 5423 are marked with a rating to indicate the maximum size of test fire that the extinguishers have been shown to control. These Class A and Class B ratings may be used to determine the number of extinguishers required in an area. BS 5306 Part 3 recommends that the aggregate Class A rating of extinguishers in an area should comprise 0.065 × floor area in square metres. Since, for example, a 9 litre water extinguisher achieves a 13A rating, each 9 litre water extinguisher may be considered to be sufficient for an area of $200m^2$. However, the aggregate rating of all extinguishers on a storey should never be less than 26A. In a large building it may, in some cases, be reasonable to reduce the number of Class A rated extinguishers if the building is also provided with hose reels.

Fire Blankets

Fire blankets are normally made from fibreglass or leather, and are contained in wall-mounted housings. They are used for extinguishing fires in people's clothing, and can be used to smother a fire involving burning food.

Their main application is, therefore, in kitchens, but fire blankets may also be found in some laboratories or areas in which people handle highly flammable liquids.

Hose Reels

Hose reels comprise a reel of rubber hose that is normally 30m in length and is permanently connected to a water supply. The relevant design code, Part 1 of BS 5306 (Hydrant systems, hose reels and foam inlets) recommends that the water supply should be capable of supplying the two highest (or, in a single storey building, the two most remote) reels at a rate of at least 24 litres/second. The pressure at the nozzle of the reel should be sufficient to enable a throw of at least six metres.

In many buildings, the water is supplied from the building's water mains, but, in higher buildings, there is a need to provide a tank and pumps as a source of supply. BS 5306 Part 1 recommends that the capacity of the tank should be at least 1125 litres and that duplicate electric pumps, which are readily available as a package, should be used.

Normally it is necessary for the user to open a valve before running out the hose. However, some hose reels have automatic valves, which provide a supply after a short, pre-determined length of hose has been run out. While these have the advantage that the user need not remember to open the valve which, if not properly maintained, can become stiff to operate, automatic valves involve additional complexity and have been known to fail when required.

Staff Training

Whatever extinguishing equipment is installed in a building, all members of staff should be properly instructed and trained in its use (except in the case of fire blankets that are only likely to be used by particular occupants, such as kitchen staff). The need for all staff to be trained is often regarded as a contentious point, and is not considered reasonable or desirable by some organisations. This view is often based on the practical problems of instructing a large number of employees, or a fear that staff may be injured if they are encouraged to fight fires.

In the opinion of the author, it is vital that all staff are trained. This view is based on the following considerations:

(a) In buildings for which a fire certificate is in force, there is normally a requirement for all staff to receive regular training in a number of fire safety matters; this usually includes the use of fire extinguishing appliances. Thus, it may be argued that failure to instruct all staff is a contravention of this legal requirement.

(b) The provision of fire extinguishing appliances for use by occupants of the premises is normally required by legislation. Section 2 of the Health and Safety at Work, etc Act 1974 requires that employers provide instruction and training to ensure, as far as reasonably practicable, the health and safety at work of the employees. The provision of extinguishers, without training in their use, could be regarded as not conducive to the safety of employees.

(c) While there should be no pressure on employees to fight fires, it is not realistic to assume that an employee will watch a small fire, perhaps in a wastepaper basket, growing, pending arrival of the fire brigade, without taking some action. For the employee's own safety and protection of the business, it is clearly desirable that the employee is reasonably capable of using extinguishing appliances.

(d) The FETA statistics described earlier in this chapter make it clear that fire extinguishing appliances make a valuable contribution to the defences against fire loss.

Checking Fire Extinguishing Appliances

All extinguishing appliances should be inspected and maintained annually by specialists. However, users should ensure on a much more regular basis that:

(a) access to hose reels and extinguishers is unobstructed
(b) manual hose reel valves are in the off position (except in the case of automatic reels) and are free from leaks
(c) all hose is neatly wound on the reel
(d) hose reel nozzles are not blocked
(e) both hose reel pumps, if provided, operate correctly
(f) all fire extinguishers are in their correct position, are undamaged, and are mounted on brackets
(g) the gauges of stored pressure extinguishers indicate normal pressure
(h) any seals on hose reel valves or extinguisher release controls are in place

(i) labels attached to the appliances indicate that maintenance has been undertaken within the last 12 months.

Further Reading

1. *BS 5306 Fire extinguishing installations and equipment on premises.*

   Part 1: Hydrant systems, hose reels and foam inlets
   Part 3: Code of practice for selection, installation and maintenance of portable fire extinguishers.
2. *Fire Safety Data Sheet PE2 Fire points.* Fire Protection Association.
3. *Fire Safety Data Sheet PE3 Fire blankets.* Fire Protection Association.
4. *Fire Safety Data Sheet PE4 Portable fire extinguishers.* Fire Protection Association.
5. *Fire Safety Data Sheet PE5 First aid fire fighting: training.* Fire Protection Association.
6. *Fire Safety Data Sheet PE7 Hose reels.* Fire Protection Association.

Chapter 12

Fixed Fire Extinguishing Systems

Types of Fixed System

A fixed fire extinguishing system is a system that is permanently installed in a building, or on an item of plant, for the purpose of extinguishing fires, either automatically or by manual initiation. Fixed fire extinguishing systems tend to be classified according to the extinguishing agent, ie water-based or aqueous extinguishing systems, and non-aqueous systems.

However, as far as applications are concerned, this division is much too crude and there is a need to consider either the actual agent, or its physical nature and the form in which it is discharged. Thus, water-based systems may be divided into the types and sub-categories shown in Table 9, while non-aqueous systems may be divided into the types and sub-categories shown in Table 10. The main applications for each system, in terms of the type of fire for which the systems are normally used is also shown.

Sprinkler Systems

Sprinklers are undoubtedly the most important and most generally applicable type of fixed extinguishing system. They are normally used for general protection throughout a building, and are commonly found in industrial and commercial premises, such as factories, warehouses and offices. In such premises, they are normally used to protect property by detecting and extinguishing any fire, or to achieve control so as to limit the fire size until the fire is extinguished by the fire brigade.

There is, however, a growing recognition of sprinklers as a life safety measure although, in the United Kingdom, sprinklers have traditionally

TYPE OF SYSTEM	MAJOR SUB-CATEGORIES	MAIN APPLICATIONS
SPRINKLER	—	CLASS A FIRES IN BUILDINGS
DRENCHER		PREVENTION OF FIRE SPREAD BETWEEN BUILDINGS
WATER SPRAY	HIGH VELOCITY	EXTINGUISHMENT OF CLASS B FIRES INVOLVING LIQUIDS WITH HIGH FLASHPOINTS (66°C AND ABOVE)
	MEDIUM VELOCITY	CONTROL OR EXTINGUISHMENT OF CLASS B FIRES INVOLVING LIQUIDS WITH LOW FLASHPOINTS (BELOW 66°C) AND WATER MISCIBLE LIQUIDS (ALSO PROTECTION OF PLANT AGAINST RADIATION FROM AN ADJACENT FIRE)
FOAM	LOW EXPANSION	CLASS B FIRES
	MEDIUM EXPANSION	CLASS B FIRES
	HIGH EXPANSION	CLASS A FIRES

Table 9: Types of water based fixed extinguishing system

TYPE OF SYSTEM	MAJOR SUB-CATEGORIES	MAIN APPLICATIONS
GASEOUS	LOCAL APPLICATION	PROTECTION OF A LOCALISED CLASS A OR CLASS B RISK WITHIN A LARGER VOLUME
	TOTAL FLOODING	PROTECTION AGAINST CLASS A OR CLASS B FIRES THROUGHOUT THE ENTIRE VOLUME OF A PROTECTED SPACE
POWDER	LOCAL APPLICATION	LOCALISED CLASS B RISKS
	TOTAL FLOODING	PROTECTION AGAINST CLASS B FIRES THROUGHOUT THE ENTIRE VOLUME OF A PROTECTED SPACE

Table 10: Types of non-aqueous fixed extinguishing system

been used mainly to protect premises where the risk to life is relatively low. It is often argued that, on a worldwide basis, loss of life in premises that are sprinklered is very rare indeed. Perhaps the classic life safety application for which sprinklers are recognised is covered shopping complexes, in which an important role of the sprinklers is to limit fire development to a size with which smoke control systems can cope (see Chapter 13).

The Need for Sprinklers

Sprinklers may be required under the Building Regulations in order to increase the permitted compartment sizes in shops (see Chapter 7). The revised Building Regulations are likely to widen the classes of occupancy to which this applies, as is already the case in Scotland. In addition, certain local legislation, such as s20 of the London Building Act (Amendment) Act, empowers local authorities to require sprinklers in certain high buildings and in large warehouses or factories.

The London District Surveyors Association (LDSA) Fire Safety Guide No 2 (*Fire Safety in Atrium Buildings*) suggests that sprinklers are essential if there is to be phased evacuation in a building that incorporates an atrium.

In any high building, there may also be a need for occupants not immediately at risk, to delay their evacuation during the course of a fire—sprinkler protection of the building could be an important measure to ensure that the fire development is controlled.

Fire insurers are very much in favour of sprinklers, particularly in industrial buildings, such as factories and warehouses. Where sprinklers are installed throughout a building, or a fire separated part of a building of this class, substantial fire insurance premium discounts can apply, provided the installation complies with the Loss Prevention Council (LPC) Rules for Automatic Sprinkler Installations, and the equipment used is of a type approved by the LPC. In large high risk buildings, some insurers may actually require sprinkler protection as a condition of insurance.

Design Codes

Until recently, the vast majority of sprinkler installations in the United Kingdom were designed and installed in accordance with the 29th Edition of the Fire Offices' Committee (FOC) *Rules for Automatic Sprinkler Installations*. Although a British Standard code of practice, BS 5306 Part 2, existed, it was not detailed, and made extensive reference to the FOC Rules.

The FOC became absorbed into the Loss Prevention Council, and subsequently the British Standard code was substantially revised so that, although its technical recommendations were virtually unchanged, it became a "stand alone" document, BS 5306 Part 2: 1990, to which reference can be made in a purchasing specification or legislative requirement. In addition, the LPC revised the FOC Rules, which are now known as the Loss Prevention Council Rules for Automatic Sprinkler Installations. The LPC basically adopted BS 5306 Part 2, which forms a substantial part of the LPC Rules.

However, the LPC Rules also incorporate a number of "Technical Bulletins", which may add to, or clarify, the contents of the British Standard. As indicated earlier in this Chapter, it is to the LPC Rules (ie the combination of the British Standard and the Technical Bulletins) that insurers will refer in making requirements or recommendations for sprinkler installations.

Sprinkler systems in the United Kingdom are sometimes designed in accordance with American codes if, for example, the building is owned by an American company, or if the company is insured by an American fire insurer. Under these circumstances, the American code used would normally be National Fire Protection Association (NFPA) Standard 13. In some circumstances, additional requirements of the American-based Factory Mutual insurers may also apply.

Components of an Installation

A schematic of a typical wet pipe sprinkler installation is shown in Figure 34. The basic components of an installation are as follows:

(a) a water supply
(b) a main valve set
(c) a network of pipes
(d) a number of sprinkler heads.

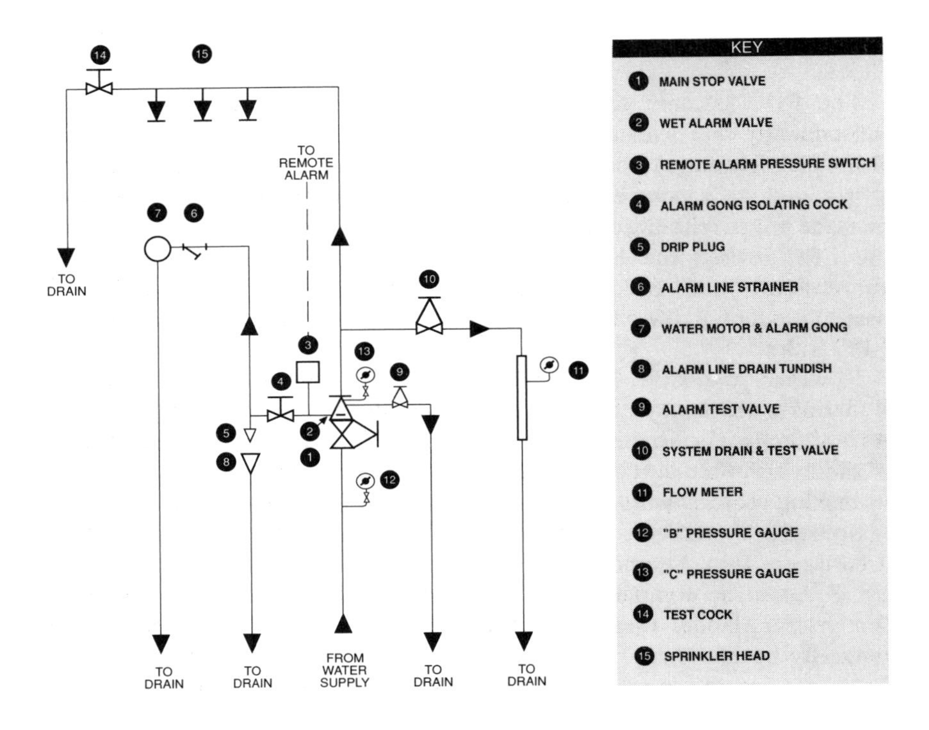

Figure 34: Wet pipe sprinkler system

Principle of Operation

Each sprinkler head is a combined heat detector and water discharge valve. When the temperature of the detecting element is sufficiently high, the valve opens, permitting water to be discharged. Each head operates entirely independently to every other head (except in installations protecting special risks, where a group of "open" heads operate simultaneously when a single valve opens, or a group of sealed heads is actuated electrically). Many fires are controlled or extinguished by the operation of only a few heads. The common view that all heads throughout a large area operate simultaneously is totally incorrect.

The sprinkler pipework is normally permanently charged with water, which is, therefore, available as soon as the first sprinkler head opens. Thus, such installations are permanently "wet". However, in unheated warehouses, for example, an "alternate" installation is sometimes used. In these systems, the pipework remains charged with water during the summer months but is drained and charged with air, becoming "dry" during the winter months. A special type of alternate valve set is required, permitting water to enter the installation pipework when the air pressure is lowered by the operation of the sprinkler head(s). In special circumstances, such as cold stores, a permanently dry installation may be required.

The main valve set comprises an installation stop valve and an alarm valve. When a sprinkler head opens and water flows into the installation, the alarm valve permits a small amount of water to flow down small bore pipework that terminates in a water driven gong, normally located outside the building, to provide a warning. A pressure switch may be fitted to this pipework, enabling the sprinkler system to connect with, for example a fire alarm system. Therefore the fire alarm system may also operate when a sprinkler head opens. Alternatively, a flow switch may be fitted to installation pipework in order to achieve the same result.

In a "pre-action" installation, dry pipework is charged with water when an automatic fire detector operates. The system may additionally operate as a conventional dry installation, in that the pipework will become charged with water even if the detector system fails to operate. The system can also be configured so that the pipework would become charged with water *only* if a fire detector operates. The pre-action valve set required is expensive, and the interface with an automatic fire detection installation reduces the inherent reliability of a wet sprinkler installation. Such systems are only used for special applications in which, for example it is necessary to speed up the operation of a dry system, or there is concern over water damage as a result of accidental damage to sprinkler heads.

Installation Design Principles

For the purpose of installation design, occupancies are divided into the following three hazard categories according to the nature of the activities and combustible materials that might be expected:

(a) light hazard
(b) ordinary hazard
(c) high hazard.

The higher the hazard category, the greater the size, and rate of development, of fire that may be anticipated. Accordingly, a different density of water discharge is required for each of the three hazard categories. Density of discharge is expressed in a similar manner to rainfall, namely in units of millimetres per minute. Since only a limited number of heads should be required to open, in order to control any fire in the premises, each hazard category has a different assumed maximum area of operation (AMAO).

Light hazard installations are relatively uncommon. They are used in non-industrial occupancies, in which the amount of combustible material is low and the building is sub-divided into spaces of limited size by fire resisting construction. In principle, the classification could apply to many areas of hospitals and hotels (which are, in fact, not normally sprinklered), libraries, museums and some offices. There is very little flexibility for changes to the building if a light hazard installation is installed. If, for example, an area containing a number of small, fire resisting cellular offices were made open plan, there could be a need to upgrade the installation to ordinary hazard. In the most hydraulically unfavourable part of the installation, the minimum design density in a light hazard installation must be 2.25mm/minute, with an AMAO of $84m^2$.

Ordinary and high hazard occupancies are further divided into sub-categories. In the case of the Ordinary Hazard sub-categories (Ordinary Hazard Groups I, II, III and III Special), the minimum design density in the most hydraulically unfavourable area of the installation is the same (5mm/minute), but the AMAO ranges from $72m^2$ to $360m^2$ respectively.

Ordinary hazard occupancies are normally industrial and commercial premises in which there is unlikely to be rapid fire development due to the nature and method of storage of the fire load. Many office buildings (excluding high rise buildings) could be classed as Ordinary Hazard Group I, provided there are no major storage areas. A typical metal working factory might be classed as Ordinary Hazard Group II, a department store would be regarded as Ordinary Hazard Group III, while a theatre would be classed as Group III Special. Typical examples of Ordinary Hazard occupancies and their groupings are given in BS 5306 Part 2, but the classification of occupancies is probably as much an art as a science, and different insurance companies may differ in their opinion on the classification of a risk. Early consultation with the insurers at the design stage of any sprinkler installation is, therefore, vital.

High hazard occupancies are those in which the process or the nature, amount, and type, of storage are such that there is a more significant challenge to the sprinkler installation. High hazard risks are divided into:

(a) process hazards
(b) high piled storage hazards
(c) potable spirit storage hazards
(d) oil and flammable liquid hazards (which, in practice would normally require special protection).

There are four categories of process hazard, for which the densities vary from 7.5mm/minute to 12.5mm/minute, according to the nature of the hazard. For three of the types of process hazard, the AMAO remains the same, and only the minimum density of discharge varies. For the fourth category, which is rare but includes firework manufacturing, BS 5306 recommends that each building be provided with complete "deluge" protection. This comprises open heads that will result in discharge of water over the entire area, on actuation of the installation.

High piled storage, high hazard occupancies are commonly warehouses. The definition of high piled varies according to the nature of the stored materials, and the minimum design density and AMAO are related to the storage height. For example, free standing flat paper would only be regarded as a high hazard risk if the storage height exceeded 4m; below this height

Ordinary Hazard Group III would apply. At the other extreme, rolls of free standing foamed rubber would require high hazard protection if stacked more than 1.2m in height. In the case of some categories and heights of high hazard racked storage, protection by ceiling mounted sprinklers alone is not regarded as sufficient; intermediate sprinklers within the storage racks may be required.

The classification of the occupancy (and the definition of the required design density and AMAO) is the first step in the specification and design of a sprinkler installation, as it will determine the nature of the water supply and the size of the pipework. As the design density and AMAO increase, a greater flow rate must be capable of being provided by the water supply. If the supply is a water authority main, it must be capable of reliably providing the required rate of flow. If it cannot do so, as is not uncommon in the case of high hazard risks or high buildings, then a tank(s) and pump(s) must be provided (see below). Again, the minimum required flow rate will determine the rating of the pump(s). In addition, since the system must be capable of supplying water for a minimum specified time, the hazard classification and rating of the pumps will determine the capacity of the tank(s).

For sufficient water to flow at a sufficient rate to the most remote area, the diameter of the pipework must be sufficient. In general, therefore, the hazard category will have a major effect on pipe sizes and, hence, the cost of the installation. There are two methods of designing the pipework. Either schedules of pipe sizes in BS 5306 Part 2 may be used or the entire installation may be hydraulically calculated (normally by means of a computer programme) to ensure that the design requirements are satisfied. The latter method offers greater flexibility in initial design, can result in a more cost effective installation, and its use is quite widespread. This method can, however, restrict future changes to the system. In the case of high piled storage with in-rack sprinklers, hydraulic calculation is essential.

Water Supplies

Water supplies for sprinkler installations normally comprise either a connection to a water authority main, or a pump(s) and tank(s) supplied from a water authority main. However, other sources of supply, including a gravity tank, a pressure tank, an elevated private reservoir and even a river or canal can, in principle, be used, although some limitations are imposed by BS 5306 Part 2.

BS 5306 divides water supplies into three categories:

(a) a single supply, such as a single town main, or single pump drawing from a tank
(b) a superior supply, such as a town main that is fed from both ends, or duplicate pumps drawing from a tank
(c) duplicate supplies, such as two independent town mains, or duplicate pumps and a tank fed from a potable water supply and suitable for a maintenance-free period of at least 15 years.

Whenever practicable, superior or duplicate supplies should be provided. Single supplies are not, in any case, acceptable for high hazard risks.

Insurers classify water supplies as Grade I, Grade II and Grade III. The lower the grade of water supply, the lower any premium discount that may apply. The three grades of supply are defined in a Technical Bulletin in the LPC Rules, and are summarised below:

A *Grade I* supply is either a duplicate supply or a superior supply (but the total number of heads, and the number in any fire compartment, is limited if a superior supply is used).
A *Grade II* supply is a superior water supply in which the limitations imposed under the definition of Grade I are not satisfied.
A *Grade III* supply is effectively a single supply, comprising a town main or a single automatic pump and tank(s).

Pumps for sprinkler systems may be either electrically driven or diesel driven. The pumps are commonly duplicated to provide either a superior or a duplicate water supply; a common arrangement is to install one diesel and one electric pump. Two electric pumps may be used, but each must then be powered from independent power supplies, or can be driven from the same supply, provided there is automatic changeover to a completely independent supply if this supply fails.

Sprinkler Heads

Sprinkler heads operate on one of two principles. *Fusible link* sprinklers open when heat from a fire melts a link that normally holds the valve closed. In the case of *glass bulb* sprinklers, a liquid-filled glass bulb holds the valve closed. Heat from a fire causes the liquid to expand, thus exerting pressure on the glass bulb, which fractures and releases the valve. Either type of head is generally acceptable.

Most conventional sprinklers can be mounted in either the pendent or upright position. Water is discharged onto a plate and is deflected in an upward and downward direction to provide ceiling wetting as well as discharge onto the fire in similar amounts. In the case of "spray heads", the discharge is predominantly downwards. BS 5306 Part 2 imposes restrictions on the use of these heads; for example, they should not be used if the roof or ceiling is combustible.

Where it is undesirable for sprinkler heads to protrude significantly below a ceiling, flush, recessed or concealed sprinklers may be considered. Flush heads are mounted so that part of the head is actually above the plane of the ceiling, but the heat sensing element remains below the ceiling. In the case of recessed heads, all or part of the sensing element is also above the ceiling. A concealed sprinkler is actually a type of recessed sprinkler with a cover plate that falls away when the head is exposed to fire. None of these sprinklers may, however, be installed for protection of high hazard risks. LPC Technical Bulletins may also prohibit the application of these heads in Ordinary Hazard Group III risks.

Special sidewall pattern sprinklers may also be used in certain applications, other than high hazard risks. These, as the name implies, are mounted in the plane of a wall, and throw water in an outward direction. They may be used, for example, in corridors or relatively small rooms in lieu of normal ceiling sprinklers.

Sprinkler heads are manufactured with a range of standard operating temperatures. Normally, the heads used in the United Kingdom operate when they reach a temperature of 68°C. The liquid in the glass bulbs of these heads is coloured red to indicate the temperature of operation. The yoke arm of standard 74°C fusible link heads is uncoloured. Sprinklers which operate at other temperatures are coded by colouring of the liquid in glass bulbs, or the yoke arms of fusible link heads, to indicate the temperature of operation.

When fire occurs, there is a significant difference between the temperature of a head and the surrounding air temperature. This is because it takes some time for the mass of the sprinkler head to become heated by the hot gases rising from the fire. Thus, two different designs of head may actually open at different times in a fire, despite being rated at the same temperature of operation. In order to reduce the delay in operation of heads in certain residential applications or high piled storage risks, a number of "fast response" heads with low thermal inertia are produced.

Location of Sprinkler Heads

Normally, if sprinkler protection is installed in a building, the entire building is covered. Partial protection of a building is unusual and should be avoided as the sprinklers in a protected area may not be able to cope with a fire that spreads from an unprotected area. Thus, if a small office is constructed in a sprinklered warehouse, for example, it must also be sprinklered.

Sprinklers should obviously be omitted from areas in which water discharge would create a serious hazard, such as in industrial areas containing molten metal. Sprinklers may also be omitted from certain electrical switchgear or transformer rooms, rooms containing oil or other flammable liquids, toilets and some staircases. However, in each case, the unprotected area must be separated from the protected area by construction that is adequately fire resisting—normally two hours fire resistance is required for walls, ceilings and floors, but doors should have a fire resistance of at least one hour,

If a building that is sprinklered communicates directly with an unsprinklered building, it is important that the fire cannot spread from the unprotected building to the protected building. Separating walls with a fire resistance of 6 hours (eg 225mm brick walls) are recommended by BS 5306 Part 2, and would be required by insurers. Openings in such walls are normally required to be protected by two fire break doors or shutters (see Chapter 7).

Sprinkler Installation Performance

The reliability of sprinkler systems to control or extinguish fire is now proven beyond doubt. Around 95% to 98% of fires that are large enough to result in sprinkler operation are controlled or extinguished by the sprinklers. Of the few per cent of sprinkler failures, many are the result of human error, such as closed stop valves, a change in hazard category without modification of the installation, improper storage practices or lack of maintenance, etc.

The reliability of sprinkler systems against false discharge is also very high. Sprinkler leakage is rare and tends to result from mechanical damage, such as impact by fork lift trucks, freezing of pipework, or excessive temperature and corrosion in aggressive industrial environments. In the benign environment of an office building, the probability of sprinkler leakage is particularly low, and conventional wet systems are sometimes even used to protect computer suites.

Checking Sprinkler Systems

BS 5306 makes the following recommendations for daily and weekly inspection and test routines:

Daily. Check:

(a) any unmonitored means of relaying fire signals to the fire brigade (see Chapter 10)
(b) certain types of pressure tank.

Weekly. Check:

(a) pressure gauge readings
(b) and test the water motor alarm and any equipment for relaying signals to the fire brigade
(c) pumps, eg fuel levels, oil levels, etc and various tests (described in BS 5306 Part 2) should be undertaken
(d) vented batteries
(e) the monitoring arrangements on stop valves of life safety systems
(f) heating systems provided to prevent freezing in the system.

These recommendations are amplified by a Technical Bulletin in the LPC Rules.

There should normally be a contract with a specialist sprinkler maintenance contractor for quarterly servicing and maintenance of the installation, unless qualified persons are available in the organisation to undertake this work.

In the course of routine safety inspections of a sprinklered building, it should be ensured that:

(a) all pipework is undamaged and that heads and pipework are free from leaks
(b) stop valves are secured in the open position
(c) goods are not stacked close to sprinkler heads
(d) no unprotected areas have been created
(e) there has been no change in the risk that would change the hazard classification
(f) sprinkler heads have not been painted.

Drencher Systems

The purpose of a drencher system is to prevent the spread of fire from a closely adjacent building to the protected building. The drencher system discharges water externally over windows and other wall openings that may permit the entry of fire to the building.

The heads may be sealed and operate in the same manner as sprinkler heads, forming an extension to the existing sprinkler installation. Alternatively, the heads may be open and are then actuated either manually or automatically by a separate detection system.

Water Spray Systems

High and medium velocity water spray systems are used where there is a fire risk due to the presence of flammable liquids. As well as automatic operation, manual control over the discharge is possible in some installations.

High velocity spray systems are used to extinguish fires in non water-miscible liquids that have relatively high flashpoints (66°C and above). The high velocity spray nozzles produce large water droplets (1.5–2.5mm diameter) that are able to penetrate the updraught from the fire and cool the liquid until it is extinguished. These systems operate in a "deluge", in that a small group of open nozzles discharge simultaneously over the risk area. Typical applications for high velocity spray systems include the protection of oil filled transformers, diesel generators and oil fired boilers.

Medium velocity spray systems are used for risks involving water-miscible flammable liquids or low flash point (less than 66°C) non water-miscible liquids. The spray heads ("sprayers") produce fine droplets (less than 0.4mm diameter) which are able to extinguish the fire by diluting the liquid and therefore raising the flashpoint of the mixture. For liquids with low flashpoints, this method is more difficult, but a measure of control is possible.

If a sufficiently fine spray is produced, heat can be extracted from the flames and the fire can be controlled. This principle is used for low flashpoint non water-miscible liquids but, again, control rather than extinguishment may be all that can be achieved.

Medium velocity spray heads are normally open and can be operated in the same manner as high velocity spray nozzles. Medium velocity spray can also be used to cool exposed structural steelwork in the event of a fire in a flammable liquids plant, or to cool flammable liquid or gas storage tanks that may be threatened by an adjacent fire. Applications for medium velocity spray systems are normally restricted to flammable liquids plants. They may also be used to protect, for example, an oil-fired boiler installation that burns fuel with a lower flashpoint than would be appropriate for a high velocity spray system.

There is no British Standard for water spray systems, but tentative rules, produced by the then Fire Offices' Committee in 1979, remain in use as a guidance document. The American NFPA Standard 15 can also be used.

Foam Systems

Foam is created by the mixture of water, air and a suitable foaming agent. Low and medium expansion foam systems are used primarily for special risk areas where quantities of flammable liquids are used or stored. It is unusual to find foam systems in general commercial and industrial buildings except, perhaps, in an oil fired boiler room.

High expansion foam systems are intended to fill the entire volume of a protected area with foam and can be used to protect Class A risks, particularly if they are inaccessible for conventional fire fighting. Such systems have, very occasionally, been used to protect the underfloor areas of computer suites, although the suitability of the medium for this application is open to debate. Most foam systems must be tailor-made for the risk. However BS 5306 Part 6 (Fire extinguishing installations and equipment on premises. Foam systems) provides further information on their design.

One particular class of foam, Aqueous Film Forming foam (AFFF), can be discharged from a sprinkler installation in order to provide more effective protection in, for example, a warehouse in which there is a large inventory of relatively low flashpoint flammable liquids. The sprinkler system is designed largely as a conventional installation with facilities for inducing the AFFF liquid into the water supply.

Gaseous Systems

Applications for Gaseous Systems

Gaseous extinguishing systems are normally used for protection of specific areas of a building, in which other extinguishing media, such as water, would be less suitable. The majority of gaseous systems are used in computer suites, rooms containing electrical plant, such as transformers or switchgear, and rooms housing sensitive electronic equipment or archive stores.

Gaseous extinguishing systems offer a number of advantages:

(a) the agents are clean and leave no residues, thereby minimising the degree of interruption to business following discharge
(b) the agents are non-conducting, making them suitable for use on live electrical equipment
(c) the agents can penetrate relatively enclosed spaces within the protected volume
(d) if operated by a suitable automatic fire detection system, the response of the extinguishing system can be fast
(e) gaseous extinguishing systems are suitable for use on both Class A and Class B fires, although extinguishment of a deep seated smouldering Class A fire is difficult and involves special system design considerations
(f) operation of the system can normally be controlled manually or automatically.

The Need for Gaseous Systems

There is generally no legislation that enables gaseous extinguishing system to be installed in a normal industrial or commercial building. However, if, for example, sprinklers are installed in a building due to the requirements of legislation, it is normally accepted that sprinkler heads may be omitted from rooms that have electrical or electronic equipment if, instead, a gaseous extinguishing system is installed in such areas.

Fire insurers normally seek the installation of a fixed fire extinguishing installation in areas in which the contents are of high value, or where a fire could result in serious financial losses. Examples are areas housing computer equipment and electronic process control equipment. Although sprinkler protection of computer rooms may be acceptable to many insurers, the use of a gaseous system provides better protection of the equipment and leads to less interruption in the event of fire. A formal scale of premium discounts does not, however, apply to gaseous systems.

Agents

The gases available for use in fixed extinguishing systems are:

(a) carbon dioxide
(b) halon 1211 (also known as bromochlorodifluoromethane, or BCF)
(c) halon 1301 (also known as bromotrifluoromethane, or BTM).

In principle, any of the agents may be used for total flooding of a protected area, such as a computer suite. In practice, halon 1211 is very rarely used for this application, and the few halon 1211 total flooding systems that exist in buildings are normally relatively old. In the United Kingdom, only carbon dioxide is used to any extent for local application systems; the gas is discharged onto a localised risk, such as a machine, within a larger volume.

In recent years, halon 1301 systems have predominated for total flooding applications. The main reason for this is the very low toxicity of the agent. Exposure to CO_2 in the concentrations used for fire extinguishment by automatic systems is lethal, and death is likely to result within seconds rather than minutes (although it must be noted that it may take a minute or more for the extinguishing concentration to be reached). However, accidental exposure of occupants to the normal design concentration of halon 1301 has been found to have no long term effects, although such exposure must still be avoided.

The reason for this dramatic difference lies in the different extinguishing mechanisms associated with the two agents. Carbon dioxide extinguishes fires by excluding the oxygen that is required for combustion. Fires involving petrol and related flammable liquids require a CO_2 concentration of 30–40%. However, where deep seated smouldering may occur in Class A materials, much higher concentrations are required. A concentration of 50% is normally specified for electrical equipment rooms, 53% for central processing areas in computer rooms, 65% for document archives, 68% for tape stores, and 75% for fur stores.

At any of the concentrations specified above, it is vital that no one enters the protected area unless the means for automatic actuation of the extinguishing system is inhibited in a reliable manner. In areas that are continuously occupied or frequently visited, the CO_2 system will normally be capable of only manual discharge, so reducing its reliability to perform on demand. This has tended to limit the use of CO_2 to areas, such as transformer rooms, that are visited infrequently and, only then, by trained persons.

Halons extinguish fire by interfering with the chemical process that occurs in flame. The efficiency of this extinguishing mechanism is such that a concentration of only 5% is normally specified for most applications. Provided the achieved concentration does not exceed 6%, the Health and Safety Executive permit the system to remain in the automatic mode of operation when the area is occupied, subject to certain safeguards. The safeguards normally include a pre-discharge warning to enable evacuation prior to discharge, and "hold off" controls that enable occupants of the protected space to delay the discharge indefinitely for as long as the hold off control is pressed.

If the concentration exceeds 6%, or if halon 1211 were used, "lock off" of the automatic mode of operation would be required before the space is occupied; at higher concentrations (or at the extinguishing concentration in the case of halon 1211), the agents have an anaesthetic effect. Sufficiently high concentrations can cause irregularity of heart rhythm, particularly if there are elevated levels of adrenalin in the bloodstream (as may occur due to the fear that a fire or gas discharge is likely to create). In practice, achieved concentrations in excess of 6%, or the use of halon 1211, are normally unnecessary.

Unfortunately, it is now accepted that halons contribute to the depletion of the ozone layer and, as discussed in Chapter 11, production is being phased out, and will effectively cease after the year 2000, except for, as yet undefined, "essential uses". These essential uses are likely to be very few in number, and are unlikely to be related to any use to which halons are currently put in typical industrial and commercial buildings.

Accordingly, the use of halons should now be avoided, except in circumstances in which no other alternative extinguishing agent or alternative fire protection strategy is suitable. Apart from environmental concerns, the installation of halon systems now may not constitute sound economics as, by the time the system is first called upon to operate (which may be many years), the availability and cost of halon for re-filling may present difficulties. Certainly, if re-filling is required after the year 2000, dependence on re-cycled halon from existing systems is likely to be necessary.

The obvious alternative to a halon system is a CO_2 system, which is just as suitable for extinguishment of fire. Nevertheless, the safety aspects of CO_2 systems cause great concern amongst potential users, many of whom are unprepared to use such systems, at least in the case of normally occupied areas. Even so, it should be stressed that the Health and Safety Executive will not normally oppose the installation of a CO_2 system that is installed in accordance with the appropriate safety features.

Research is currently in progress into the use of new alternative agents with little or no ozone depleting potential. Ideally, any new such agent would be suitable for direct replacement of halon 1301 in existing systems without significant modification of the system (the so-called "drop in" replacement). However, the future availability of a halon 1301 replacement that has the same fire extinguishing efficiency, has low toxicity and presents no potential for ozone depletion is, perhaps, unlikely.

Design Codes

Gaseous systems in the United Kingdom are invariably designed in accordance with the relevant part of BS 5306 (Fire extinguishing installations and equipment on premises). Part 5 of the standard contains design guidance on halon total flooding systems. Section 5.1 deals with systems that use halon 1301, while Section 5.2 is concerned with halon 1211 systems. Part 4 is concerned with carbon dioxide fixed systems, and deals with total flooding and local application systems (as well as manual hose reel installations).

The British Standard incorporates advice on requirements for personnel safety. However, detailed guidance on the subject is contained in Health and Safety Executive Guidance Note GS16 (Gaseous fire extinguishing systems: precautions for toxic and asphyxiating hazards).

Components of an Installation

A typical gaseous extinguishing system comprises:

- an agent storage facility
- means of automatic fire detection (associated with a means for initiating gas discharge)
- manual release controls
- a network of pipes and discharge nozzles (see Figure 35)
- means for switching the installation from the automatic/manual mode of operation to the manual-only mode
- means for total isolation of the system.

The gas storage facility usually comprises a central bank of storage cylinders, normally sited outside the protected area (although, in small "modular" halon systems, one or more small containers are distributed throughout the protected area). The gas is stored in the cylinders as a liquid under pressure. In very large CO_2 installations, the gas may, instead, be stored at lower pressure in a refrigerated tank.

The automatic fire detection arrangement may comprise a separate self contained automatic fire detection system (see Chapter 10); BS 7273 Part 1 (Code of practice for the operation of fire protection measures. Electrical actuation of gaseous total flooding extinguishing systems) gives advice on the interface between the fire detection and fire extinguishing systems.

Simple mechanical means of detection and automatic release of gas are also possible, and are sometimes used in small CO_2 installations. In this case, the method of detection usually comprises, for example, one or more fusible links located in the protected area. These links are attached to a wire under tension. When a fusible link melts in a fire, the tension on the wire is released, and this permits a weight to fall, actuating the mechanical discharge release control as it does so. A further part of BS 7273 will deal specifically with such mechanically actuated gaseous extinguishing installations.

In electrically actuated systems, the manual discharge control normally comprises a "two action" device (eg lift flap/break glass) that opens or closes an electrical circuit. In mechanically actuated systems, a mechanical pull handle is normally provided. In either case, these devices are normally situated outside the exits from the protected area. In the case of an electrically

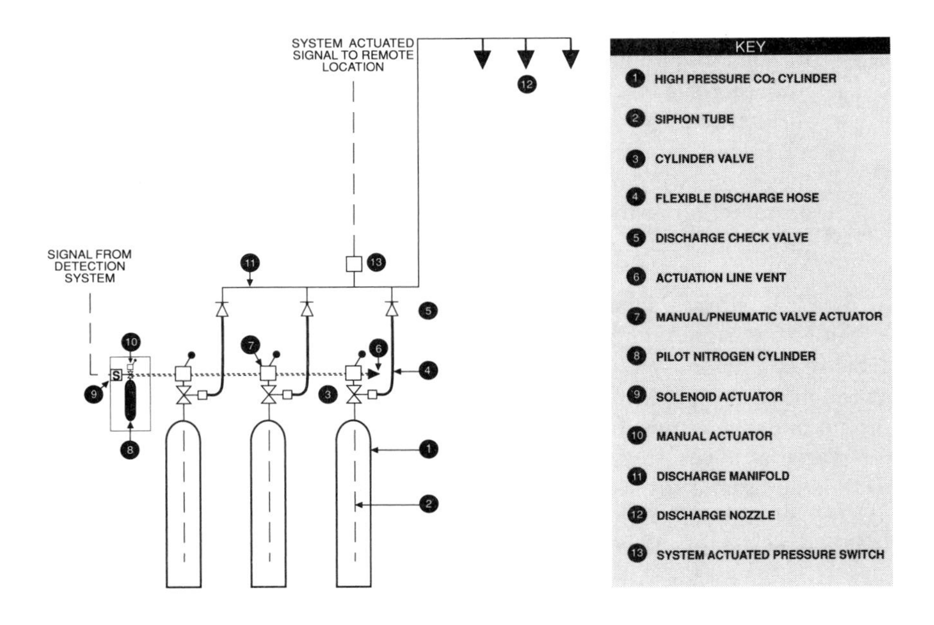

Figure 35: Automatic carbon dioxide system

operated system, a three-way illuminated status display unit, indicating whether the system is in the automatic/manual mode or manual only mode of operation, and providing a warning if gas has been discharged, should also be located at each entrance to the protected area.

Powder Systems

In principle, powder systems are suitable for total flooding or local application in areas that contain either Class A or Class B risks. In practice, powder systems are rare, and their use is mainly in local application for Class B risks, including deep fat fryers (for which foams and other special "wet chemical" systems may also be used). However, special localised Class A risks, such as textile machines, have been successfully protected by powder systems for many years. Also, powder systems have been used for other Class B risks, including road tanker filling bays. Guidance on the design of powder systems is contained in Part 7 of BS 5306 (Specification for powder systems).

Further Reading

1. *BS 5306 Fire extinguishing installations and equipment on premises.*

   Part 0: Guide to the selection of installed systems and other fire equipment.
   Part 4: Specification for carbon dioxide systems.
   Part 5: Halon systems
   Section 5.1 Halon 1301 total flooding systems
   Section 5.2 Halon 1211 total flooding systems
   Part 6: Foam systems
   Section 6.1 Specification for low expansion foam systems
   Section 6.2 Specification for medium and high expansion foam systems
2. *Fire Safety Data Sheet PE6 The Choice of fixed fire extinguishing systems.* Fire Protection Association
3. *Fire Safety Data Sheet PE9 Automatic sprinklers: on introduction.* Fire Protection Association

4. *Fire Safety Data Sheet PE10 Automatic sprinklers: components of a system*. Fire Protection Association
5. *Fire Safety Data Sheet PE11 Automatic sprinklers: design and installation*. Fire Protection Association
6. *Fire Safety Data Sheet PE12 Automatic sprinklers: care and maintenance*. Fire Protection Association
7. *Fire Safety Data Sheet PE13 Automatic sprinkler systems: safety during sprinkler shutdown*. Fire Protection Association
8. *Rules for automatic sprinkler installations*. Loss Prevention Council
9. *Health and Safety Executive Evidence Note GS16 Gaseous fire extinguishing systems: precautions for toxic asphyxiating hazards*. HMSO

Chapter 13

Smoke Control

The Threat from Smoke

The need for measures to control smoke generated by a fire arises from the serious threat that smoke alone can create to people, property and the operation of many businesses. More people die from the inhalation of smoke and toxic gases than from direct burns. The toxic gases produced by most fires include carbon monoxide, the inhalation of which is a common cause of deaths in fires. Indeed, even when other toxic gases are present, such as hydrogen cyanide, the presence of carbon monoxide is likely to remain the main cause of death.

Before the inhalation of smoke becomes lethal, it can create severe irritation to the respiratory system. In non-lethal concentrations carbon monoxide will affect a person's ability to concentrate properly. One of the earliest dangers that smoke creates, however, is loss of visibility. It has been shown that people are unwilling to attempt to move through smoke which may be present in a corridor, unless the visibility is adequate, even though passage through the smoke may be possible without serious injury. Loss of visibility may, therefore, cause people to be trapped by fire and, as a result, suffer injury or death at a later stage.

Smoke also creates great difficulties for firefighters. Although the use of breathing apparatus can make entry into a smoke filled building possible, poor visibility can lead to injury to firefighters, who are unable to see hazards within the smoke filled area. Locating the seat of the fire is also difficult in smoke filled conditions, and thus smoke constitutes an obstacle to the fire brigade in limiting the extent of fire and water damage.

Smoke damage (as opposed to direct fire damage) may also contribute a very significant proportion of the damage to the contents of a building, particularly in, for example, a food warehouse, or if the contents of a building include sensitive electronic equipment. In any building, however, smoke from a fire is likely to require, at the very least, cleaning of surfaces and contents, and may ultimately lead to the onset of long term corrosion of metalwork. In the case of smoke damage to a critical facility, such as a computer suite, the effects of smoke can lead to substantial business interruption while the affected equipment is either cleaned or replaced.

The Spread of Smoke

In the very early stages of a fire, substantial spread of smoke beyond the room of origin may occur simply due to an open door. As the fire develops and pressures are created by the expanding gases, the fit of any closed doors in their frames becomes important—smoke will tend to flow through any gaps due to the pressure differential that is created across the door. Unstopped service penetrations in the barriers that enclose the room are also an important route for smoke spread. Once smoke spreads beyond the room of origin, it will flow unimpeded along corridors, up staircases and service ducts or shafts until, ultimately, a large part of the building may become smoke logged, unless checked by suitable construction.

The spread of smoke from a fire can be controlled to a lesser or greater extent by various measures. Some measures are simple, straightforward and incorporated in most buildings as a basic design feature, while others are more sophisticated. Whatever the measures provided, their purpose and mode of operation must be understood by the person who is responsible for the building, and it must be ensured that maintenance of the facilities is adequate.

The Nature of Smoke Control Measures

The choice of smoke control measures may depend on their objectives, for example:

(a) protecting the means of escape
(b) assisting the fire brigade
(c) limiting damage to the building and its contents.

Smoke control can be achieved by one of two methods. Either the smoke produced by a fire can be *contained* within the area of fire origin, or the smoke can be *ventilated*. Smoke control measures of both types may be regarded as either fundamental (ie incorporated into most building designs) or special (ie more sophisticated, and necessary only in certain applications). Although the sub-division of measures in this way is somewhat arbitrary, examples of fundamental and special means of providing smoke containment or smoke ventilation are shown in Table 11.

Smoke Containment by Physical Barriers

Physical barriers, such as walls and partitions are the simplest means of containing smoke. If all partitions that enclose a corridor extend to at least the level of any false ceiling, smoke movement can be prevented in the early stages of a fire. As the fire progresses there is a need for the barriers to be fire resisting, in order to continue their smoke control function. There is also a need for penetrations in barriers (eg for the passage of services) to be fire stopped to prevent leakage of smoke through the gaps around the services. In addition, the walls need to make contact with the true ceiling slab.

A tightly fitting door will assist in the limitation of smoke spread in the very early stages of a fire. As the fire develops, the pressure difference across the door may result in smoke passing through gaps around the door; such gaps should be minimised. All doors that are specifically intended to resist the passage of smoke should be fitted with smoke seals (see Chapter 7). If the door's smoke control function is to continue for any significant length of time, the door and seal must be fire resisting.

As some smoke will inevitably leak around a door, two doors between the fire and the area that is to be protected, will enhance the level of protection. This is sometimes known as the principle of "two door separation", but is often referred to as "lobbying", as the two doors usually form a lobby between accommodation and an escape or firefighting staircase (see Chapter 14). Two door separation can be achieved, however, by enclosing a corridor that approaches the staircase in fire resisting construction. In some cases, ventilation of the lobby is necessary to afford additional, effective protection.

	EXAMPLES OF SMOKE CONTAINMENT MEASURES		EXAMPLE OF SMOKE VENTILATION MEASURES	
OBJECTIVE	FUNDAMENTAL	SPECIAL	FUNDAMENTAL	SPECIAL
PROTECTION OF MEANS OF ESCAPE	Well fitting solid doors with smoke seals and a reasonable degree of fire resistance Fire resisting enclosures for "protected" routes Fire stopping of penetrations in barriers that enclose escape routes Lobbies in certain circumstances	Pressurisation of escape routes		Natural ventilation or mechanical smoke extraction facilities
ASSISTANCE FOR THE FIRE BRIGADE	Lobbies for firefighting staircases	Pressurisation of firefighting staircases	Permanent ventilation and openable windows	Natural ventilation or mechanical smoke extraction facilities
DAMAGE LIMITATION	Fire resisting barriers and fire resisting doors with smoke seals Lobbies in certain circumstances Fire stopping of fire resisting barriers			Natural ventilation or mechanical smoke extraction facilities

Table 11: Examples of smoke control measures

Smoke Containment by Pressurisation

The presence of physical barriers may not offer a sufficiently high degree of protection. Examples are buildings in which the number of staircases is insufficient, or buildings where the firefighting staircase is not ventilated or extends deep below ground level. In these cases, pressurisation may be a suitable measure.

Pressurisation involves the injection of air into escape routes (staircases or corridors) in order to increase the pressure in the escape routes, compared with that in the adjacent accommodation. The result is that this excess pressure opposes and overcomes that created by the fire, permitting a constant flow of air from the escape route into the accommodation, instead of a flow of smoke from the accommodation into the escape route. This technique is now well recognised and has been found to operate successfully both in tests and in actual fires. Guidance on the design of pressurisation systems is contained in BS 5588 Part 4 (Fire precautions in the design of buildings. Smoke control in protected escape routes using pressurisation).

Smoke Ventilation

It is normal practice to provide smoke ventilation facilities within the accommodation and staircases in a building, by means of openable windows. For most staircases, a suitably sized vent at the top of the staircase is accepted as an alternative. In firefighting staircases, ventilation at the top, and means for providing ventilation at each storey, are normally required unless the staircase is pressurised. The lobbies to these staircases should also be provided with both permanent ventilation and means for providing additional ventilation at each storey level. Where natural ventilation of staircases or lobbies cannot be provided direct to open air, ventilation may, instead, be via smoke shafts or, in the case of basements, breakable covers at pavement level.

It should be stressed that the ventilation described in these cases is not to aid means of escape, but is intended to be of assistance to the fire brigade at a stage following evacuation. The objective of the ventilation is either to maintain a smoke free access route for the fire brigade, or to purge the building of smoke after the fire has been extinguished.

In large volume, single storey warehouse buildings and similar premises, the provision of smoke ventilation may be useful as an aid to the fire brigade, by keeping the base of the smoke layer at a sufficient height, so maintaining a reasonable degree of visibility at head height and below. Such facilities may be required under certain Local Acts (see Chapter 1). Ventilation facilities normally comprise vents that open automatically when a fusible link melts. However, the smoke vents can be of a type that operate either by a smoke detection system or by manual controls. Powered smoke extraction fans may be provided as an alternative but require reliable power supplies, fire protected wiring, and fans that can withstand high temperatures. However, powered extraction is much less susceptible than natural ventilation to external wind pressures.

Natural ventilation or extraction of smoke may be found in other special applications. Perhaps the most important of these is the case of covered shopping complexes, in which a form of smoke ventilation, often involving powered extraction, is invariably required to maintain a smoke free area at head height and below in the mall during the evacuation of the centre.

Atrium buildings are another example in which natural ventilation or powered extraction is normally required. In this case, however, the atrium space itself will not necessarily form part of the means of escape, and the facilities may be most relevant to smoke removal from the atrium as a means of assistance to the fire brigade and to prevent undue alarm on the part of occupants. In the case of a relatively tall atrium building, it is likely that powered extraction, as opposed to natural ventilation, will be appropriate.

Further Reading

1. *BRE Digest 260 Smoke control in buildings: design principles.* Building Research Establishment.

Chapter 14

Fire Brigade Facilities

Fire brigade facilities may be provided to assist firefighters in tackling a fire and, if necessary, effecting rescues. In some cases, these facilities may be required by legislation, such as Building Regulations or Local Acts. Liaison with the fire brigade concerning any facilities provided for their benefit is clearly wise, and the Fire Services Act 1947 requires fire authorities to give advice on such matters on request.

It is also important to make local fire brigade crews familiar with the building and any special facilities, so that the brigade can perform as efficiently as possible in the event that they are summoned to a fire in the premises. Again, fire brigades are required by the Fire Services Act to make themselves aware of information concerning property in their area, the available water supplies, the means of access, etc. Normally, fire brigades do this by means of familiarisation visits to the premises (often known as 1(1)(d) visits, after the clause of the Fire Services Act that makes them necessary).

Facilities that may be provided to assist the fire brigade include:

(a) access arrangements, including firefighting staircases and lifts
(b) dry or wet rising mains and foam inlets
(c) private water supplies
(d) smoke ventilation and plant shutdown facilities
(e) relevant information for use at the time of a fire
(f) special communications facilities
(g) fireman's emergency switches in circuits supplying exterior electrical installations, or interior discharge lighting installations, if, in either case, the installations operate at a voltage exceeding low voltage.

Access for Fire Appliances

At the design stage of a new building, it is important to ensure that there will be adequate access arrangements to enable fire appliances to approach the building. Access requirements can be imposed under local legislation and, in Scotland, under the powers of building control. In England and Wales, the revised Building Regulations will contain requirements on the subject.

Conditions imposed for access by the fire brigade are concerned with the practicalities of firefighting. Different requirements apply according to whether or not the building is fitted with rising mains (see below). It should be noted, however, that there may be a need for rescue by ladder or aerial appliance (turntable ladder or hydraulic platform), and this should be taken into account at the design stage, regardless of the existence of legislative controls. Private roadways and access gates to sites should be designed to take into account the need for access by fire appliances. Guidance on detailed requirements for access may be obtained from the local authority fire brigade.

Access for Firefighters

The most important design requirement regarding access for firefighters is that relating to staircases and lifts. It is generally accepted that, for efficient firefighting in a high building or a building with deep basements, there must be a number of smoke-free staircases, known as firefighting staircases. Between each landing of a firefighting staircase and the accommodation, there must be provided a firefighting lobby, which forms a "bridgehead" for attack by the fire brigade. In order to enable firefighters to transport hose and equipment to the higher floors of the building, there should also be one or more firefighting lifts, which will continue to operate reliably during the course of the fire.

The staircase, lobby and lift are enclosed within a fire resisting envelope, normally described as a firefighting shaft. The firefighting shaft also contains dry or wet rising mains (see below). A firefighting shaft, without a lift or rising main, may also be of assistance to the fire brigade in a building that is not particularly high but is large in area, thereby making firefighting from outside the building more difficult.

A firefighting staircase is normally a staircase that is in everyday use by occupants of the building, and forms part of the means of escape. It is, however, afforded special protection to ensure that it remains smoke free during a fire. Not every protected staircase in a building need necessarily form a firefighting staircase. A firefighting lift will normally be a conventional passenger lift (but not a goods lift) that is of sufficient size to carry fire brigade equipment, that can be grounded quickly in the event of fire and brought under the control of the operator in the lift, and that has power supplies that can maintain the operation of the lift during the fire.

Recommendations for firefighting shafts are contained in BS 5588 Part 5 (Fire precautions in the design, use and construction of buildings. Code of practice for firefighting stairways and lifts). The code recommends that:

(a) firefighting shafts, incorporating firefighting lifts and rising (or falling) mains should be provided in all buildings, or parts of buildings, exceeding 18m in height or 9m depth below ground
(b) if a building is used for trade, warehousing or manufacturing, and exceeds 7.5m in height, with a floor area of any above ground storey exceeding $600m^2$, a firefighting shaft should be provided. In this case, however, the shaft need only contain a firefighting stairway and firefighting lobby, but not a firefighting lift or rising main
(c) on each storey of height above, or depth below, the above figures, there should be one firefighting shaft for every $900m^2$. The distance from the furthest point in a storey to the door of the nearest firefighting shaft, measured along the route that hose would follow, should not exceed 60m.

The importance of ensuring the integrity of the power supplies to a firefighting lift cannot be over emphasised. BS 5588 Part 5 contains detailed recommendations on this matter. The most important design aspects are:

(a) the availability of an alternative power supply to cater for failure of the normal supply
(b) protection of cables providing power to the lift
(c) means for ensuring that the cables of the primary supply and the alternative supply cannot both be affected by a single fire.

The lift installation must have a switch at the fire brigade access level (to cause the lift to be returned to the fire brigade access level, after which it can only be controlled from within the lift car). There must also be a means of communication between the lift car, the fire brigade access level and the lift machine room.

Arrangements for access to any large building or site should be discussed with the enforcing authority so that access can be suitably pre-planned. Such liaison also ensures that any potential conflicts between security and the need for access by the fire brigade in the event of fire can be overcome. In a large building, there may be many more fire exits than normal access doors. For security reasons, many of the fire exits may be openable only from the inside. In the event of a need for access via such doors (for example, to provide an additional approach by which the fire may be attacked) they can often be forced open by the fire brigade. However, valuable time can be saved if the doors are fitted with locks that are readily openable from the inside (eg by a panic bar), but can also be opened from the outside by means of keys held on the premises.

Rising and Falling Mains

In high buildings, it would be time consuming and difficult to run a hose from a hydrant in the street to the higher floors of the building. The same difficulty applies in the case of very deep basements and buildings to which access by a fire appliance is not possible. In these circumstances, fire mains are provided. A dry fire main comprises an inlet, located externally, to which the fire brigade connect a line of hose from the nearest hydrant, and outlets, known as landing valves, on each floor of the building. The fire brigade take lengths of hose into the building, and connect them to the landing valves, thereby obtaining a source of water for firefighting without the need to run hose from the street to the seat of the fire.

Dry fire mains that serve the upper floors of high buildings are known as *dry rising mains*, while those serving the lower floors of a building with deep basements are known as *dry falling mains*. In very high buildings, the rising mains are permanently charged with water, supplied by pumps in the building. These mains are known as *wet rising mains*.

Fire mains in high buildings, or those with deep basements, are normally provided only in those buildings with a firefighting lift, and the landing valves are located in the firefighting lobbies (see above). Accordingly, BS5588 Part 5 recommends that fire mains be provided in buildings that are greater than 18m in height, or those that contain floors greater than 9m below ground level.

Detailed guidance on the design of dry and wet fire mains is contained in BS 5306 Part 1 (Fire extinguishing installations and equipment on premises. Hydrant systems, hose reels and foam inlets).

Where mains are required, dry rising mains are recommended by the code, except in the case of buildings exceeding 60m in height, for which wet rising mains are recommended. A dry rising main is normally 100mm in diameter, unless there is more than one outlet per floor, in which case a 150mm diameter main is recommended by the Code. Wet rising mains should be capable of supplying three firefighting jets for a period of at least 45 minutes when the total water demand is 1500 litres/minute. A town main will not normally be adequate to satisfy this criterion, and the water supply normally comprises duplicate pumps drawing from a tank of at least 45,000 litres capacity, which is filled from a town main. Domestic water tanks are not suitable for this purpose, unless it can be ensured that the above quantity will always remain and cannot be used to meet the needs of the domestic supply.

Rising mains should be inspected by competent persons every six months. Every year, dry rising mains should be charged with water to check for leaks.

Foam Inlets

Foam inlets enable the fire brigade to inject foam into areas at or below ground level in which there is a risk of an oil fire. Common examples are oil fired boiler rooms and oil storage tank rooms. A system of fixed piping is installed, with outlets in the risk area, and an inlet(s), for use by the fire brigade, externally on a wall of the building. Guidance on foam inlets is contained in BS 5306 Part 1.

Private Water Supplies

If the hose reels on pumping appliances (supplied from water tanks carried on the appliances) are not sufficient to control a fire, lines of hose are usually set into public fire hydrants on water authority mains. These are capable of supplying water at a much higher rate than the hose reels. On a large private site, such as a major factory, however, the nearest public hydrant may be some distance away. In this case, there may be a need for the occupier of the site to provide private water supplies for use by the fire brigade.

Private water supplies normally comprise hydrants on the site's private underground water mains. The hydrants are normally sited adjacent to roadways, and should preferably be fed from a ring main, enabling the hydrant to be fed in two directions. Guidance on private fire hydrants is contained in BS 5306 Part 1, which recommends that such hydrants should not be sited closer than 6m, nor further than 70m, from the buildings that they serve. The maximum distance between hydrants should not be greater than 150m, and the water supply should, ideally, be capable of supplying 1500 litres/minute. The locations of private hydrants should be marked by suitable signs, and should be inspected and tested every year to ensure that they remain adequate for use by the fire brigade.

Where suitable water mains are not available, static and natural sources of water supply may be considered. In practice, the fire brigade may have pre-planned the use of sources such as a river, canal, lake, etc, but liaison with the fire brigade may lead to measures, such as sumps and hard standing for portable pumps, which may assist the brigade's operational use of these supplies. If, on consultation with the fire brigade, it is revealed that a shortfall of water may, nevertheless, exist, consideration may be given to the provision of a dedicated emergency water supply, such as a strategically sited water tank of suitable capacity.

Smoke Control Facilities

In order to remove smoke, the fire brigade may need to open windows in the building. Any windows or vents that the fire brigade may require to open, should be fitted with simple lever handles. Sealed, air conditioned buildings should be fitted with locks that can be opened with a square-ended key. If the windows or vents are not accessible, they should be provided with a remote control facility that is suitably marked and located at a position agreed with the fire brigade. Further information on smoke control facilities is given in Chapter 13.

In modern buildings with complex air conditioning systems, there should be facilities that enable the fire brigade to shut down or modify the air flows. Any such facilities, and any special facilities for smoke ventilation or extraction, should be discussed with the fire brigade at the design stage. In addition, local fire crews should be made familiar with the location and operation of the facilities.

Information for the Fire Brigade

In the case of a large building or site, it may be of great assistance to the fire brigade if they are provided with information on the building, its layout, any hazardous storage, and the locations of service controls, sprinkler stop valves, etc. Much of this information can be provided in the form of plans drawn up in consultation with the fire brigade, to be used by the brigade at the time of a fire. The plans may then be kept in a suitably labelled container within, for example, the entrance hallway of a building or at a reception desk. This does not, however, obviate the need for a responsible person to meet and assist the brigade on their arrival (see Chapter 17). In some areas, local legislation may also require that basement plans are displayed in the building. The provision of signs to indicate the presence of potentially hazardous materials is also advisable, and may be required by the relevant enforcing authority.

Communications Facilities

Although the fire brigade have portable radios available to them for use in buildings, in large, complex buildings, and in areas in which radio transmission could prove difficult, a dedicated communications system can be of great benefit. Consideration should, therefore, be given to the provision of facilities, such as dedicated telephones, between firefighting lobbies, and a suitable control point at the fire brigade access level. Since these facilities are required to operate during a fire, the cable used or its method of protection, should be such as to ensure that failure during the course of a fire is unlikely.

Fireman's Emergency Switches

The IEE Wiring Regulations require that fireman's emergency switches be provided in the low voltage circuits supplying:

(a) exterior electrical installations operating at a voltage exceeding low voltage
(b) interior discharge lighting installations operating at a voltage exceeding low voltage.

The provision of these switches may also be required by legislation.

Further Reading

1. *BS 5306 Part 1 Fire extinguishing installations and equipment on premises.* Hydrant systems, hose reels and foam inlets.
2. *BS 5588 Part 5 Fire precautions in the design, use and construction of buildings.* Code of practice for firefighting stairways and lifts.
3. *Fire Prevention Design Guide 5: Firefighting facilities for the fire brigade.* Fire Protection Association.

Chapter 15

Management of Fire Safety

Fire safety cannot be passively managed, nor can it simply be left for third parties, such as enforcing authorities or insurers, to impose at the time of periodic surveys. Equally, the provision of fire protection equipment does not, by itself, lead to adequate fire safety standards. Fire safety must be monitored, controlled and actively managed.

The monitoring and control of fire safety is indisputably a management responsibility. It should not be regarded as an "add on" duty, needing only concentrated attention on an infrequent basis. Fire safety should be an integral part of day-to-day management, emanating from the highest level of management. Too often, fire safety measures originate from lower level management, who struggle to compete for the attention of more senior management, with the result that, if improvements are not actually positively blocked, they remain in prolonged abeyance.

What is involved in the management of fire safety? Management aspects of fire safety percolate through virtually every chapter of this book, from ensuring that proposed changes to the means of escape are passed to the fire authority (see Chapter 1), to arranging for training of staff in fire safety matters and carrying out fire drills (see Chapter 18).

If fire safety were a priority throughout the management activities of every company, there would be little need to highlight the subject of management in a book on fire safety. Such a world does not, of course, exist. Experience shows that a major contributing factor to multiple death fires in modern industrial or commercial buildings is inadequate management of fire safety—rather than inadequate building design or failure of fire protection equipment.

Countless committees of inquiry into fire disasters have determined that management deficiencies played at least a significant role in the outcome of the fire, if not the major role. Examples include the following disasters:

Summerland leisure complex, Isle of Man, where 50 people died in a fire in 1973. Criticisms made included:

(a) no overall duty in respect of fire safety
(b) no staff training in fire safety
(c) long delay in summoning the fire brigade
(d) no organised methodical evacuation
(e) locked fire exits
(f) misguided actions by staff
(g) delay in operating the fire alarm system.

Stardust Discotheque, Dublin, where 48 people died in a fire in 1981. Criticisms made included:

(a) no emergency evacuation plan
(b) employees not allocated specific duties in the event of fire
(c) staff as confused as patrons during the fire
(d) exits were locked or gave the impression of being locked
(e) delay in summoning the fire brigade
(f) actions of staff uncoordinated and inadequate
(g) failure to operate the fire alarm system.

It remains the case in many organisations that the responsibility for fire safety is, as in the case of Summerland, unclear or undefined. As a result, there is a lack of co-ordination of fire safety matters. While some aspects of fire safety probably receive proper attention, some may "fall between two stools" because they do not neatly fall into the category of either building management or building maintenance. Committees of inquiry and criminal or civil courts of law tend to find much less difficulty in determining responsibility after a serious fire has occurred or when serious deficiencies in fire safety come to light. There appears to be a positive trend towards placing responsibility squarely on the shoulders of management. In his report on the King's Cross Fire in 1987, Mr Desmond Fennell QC found that:

> . . . London Transport at its highest level may not have given as high a priority to passenger safety in stations as it should have done.

The part of the Fennell report devoted to the management of safety found that no one person was charged with overall responsibility for safety. However, it is not only disasters that lead to the retrospective imposition of responsibility for fire safety. In a recent case, the assistant manager of a London bookshop received a suspended prison sentence (and hence a criminal record) for deficiencies in the shop's fire safety.

A defined responsibility for fire safety, or at least its effective control, is, therefore, an important basis for the management of fire safety in any organisation. In a large organisation, operational control of fire safety may be delegated to a professional fire safety manager, who may also manage safety and security. In a smaller organisation, operational control may lie with a director, personnel manager, chief engineer, etc. The actual position probably matters little, provided there is an adequate budget for fire safety measures and the manager responsible:

(a) is aware of his or her responsibilities
(b) is given authority to exert influence over all aspects of fire safety
(c) is allocated adequate time to devote to fire safety
(d) has adequate knowledge or ready access to specialist advice
(e) has support from senior management to develop and implement policies.

The formulation of clear fire safety policies is fundamental to the management of fire safety. Such policies must be based on an understanding that the risk from fire is a *pure* risk (ie can only result in loss), as opposed to a *speculative* risk (which can result in profit or loss). Policies on fire safety must be tailor made for the needs of the organisation and the potential for loss that it faces.

The simplest possible policy is that the company should comply only with the minimum fire safety requirements set by legislation. Such requirements will relate primarily to life safety. The risk of property damage, and often business interruption, is then managed by the purchase of insurance. While such a policy appears to be relatively simple, its strict implementation may be much more complex. There is a vast difference in the amount of time and effort devoted to fire safety by an organisation that considers compliance with legislation to involve merely obtaining a fire certificate, and the much greater time and effort devoted by an organisation in which the fire certificate is read thoroughly and its requirements are implemented exactly.

In more informed organisations, the risk from fire will have been correctly identified, and the consequences of fire will be well understood. This will often lead to clearly defined policies regarding protection of assets and critical facilities, which supplement the basic requirements of legislation for protection of life. Thus, a group may decide that the potential for fire loss in their large storage buildings is such that all large storage buildings in the group should be sprinklered. Such a decision may have been taken in conjunction with the group's insurance advisers, who would be in a position to provide guidance on the "payback" in terms of fire insurance premiums. At a more detailed level, the critical nature of the group's data processing installations may require the halon gas flooding systems to be set to automatic at all times—requiring special safeguards for the areas' occupants (see Chapter 12).

However, just as management of a company's finances does not end with the formulation of accounting and investment policies, management of fire safety does not end with the formulation of policy. It must be ongoing and routine. Unfortunately, good (and bad) fire safety management is probably easier to recognise than describe, given the diversity of the activities involved. There is no single relevant British Standard to which the manager can turn for definitive advice and much of the information and guidance that a manager requires is dispersed throughout many different codes and standards. Nevertheless, excellent straightforward and simple guidance documents, which do not require substantial amounts of reading time, are produced by the Loss Prevention Council. In particular, attention is drawn to FPA fire safety data sheets in the MR (Management of Fire Risks) series.

In assessing the standard of fire safety management in an organisation, attention should focus on:

(a) in every building, a defined responsibility for fire safety
(b) suitable and well documented fire procedures (see Chapter 17)
(c) training of staff in fire matters (see Chapter 18)
(d) appointment of fire wardens if appropriate (see Chapters 17 and 18)
(e) properly conducted fire drills (see Chapter 18)
(f) regular in-house fire safety inspections (see Chapter 16)

(g) contracts or other formal arrangements for inspection, testing and maintenance of fire protection equipment (see Chapter 16)
(h) proper inspection, testing and maintenance of plant and equipment, including electrical installations (see Chapter 5)
(i) close control over the activities of outside contractors (see Chapter 5)
(j) proper procedures during hazardous activities such as hot work (see Chapter 5)
(k) regular liaison with the operational personnel of the local fire brigade, and pre-planning for assisting the brigade in the event of fire (see Chapter 14)
(l) liaison with the fire brigade if changes to the premises are required, and notification of the fire brigade when "material" changes are proposed (see Chapter 1)
(m) records of inspections, tests and maintenance of fire protection euqipment, training of staff, fire drills, etc
(n) policies concerning smoking (see Chapter 5)
(o) good standards of fire prevention (see Chapter 5)
(p) good standards of housekeeping
(q) recognition and control of hazardous substances
(r) contingency plans for fire or other emergency.

Housekeeping standards are particularly relevant to fire safety. Housekeeping relates to the tidiness, order and general conditions within the building. Untidily strewn packaging materials that obstruct an exit route obviously constitute bad housekeeping, but of equal importance is attention to detail, eg the provision of drip trays where flammable liquids are dispensed from drums.

Comment and opinion on housekeeping form an important part of reports produced by the fire surveyors of insurance companies. The surveyor's views on housekeeping provide the insurance underwriter with an indication of the management standards (which may also appear as a particular item in the report). The standard of management is considered to be significant in the assessment of the level of risk. In fact, particularly good housekeeping, or particularly bad housekeeping, may actually influence the insurance premium charged.

Housekeeping standards are important as they affect most aspects of fire safety, in particular fire prevention. Chapter 5 described hazards such as rubbish stored close to buildings, trailing leads to electrical appliances, storage close to light fittings, the build up of grease deposits in kitchens, etc—all of which increase the probability that a fire will occur.

Bad housekeeping can also affect the manner in which fire develops. If a fire starts in a neatly stacked pile of timber pallets, around which there is a clear space, the fire may be spotted and extinguished before it can spread. If the same pallets were strewn around in an untidy heap with adjacent rubbish, it is likely that the fire would spread over a larger area and involve further combustible materials.

Bad housekeeping may also impede the effectiveness of the fire protection measures that would otherwise limit the injury and damage caused by fire. For example, the efficiency of escape routes and exits, fire exit signs and emergency lighting will be threatened if they are obstructed or obscured.

Rapid access to fire equipment, such as manual call points, extinguishers and hose reels may also be prevented by bad housekeeping. Even if access is not positively prevented, if it takes longer to raise the alarm or reach an extinguisher, the fire will be larger before occupants can escape or extinguishers can be used.

The effectiveness of automatic fire protection systems may also be impaired by bad housekeeping. The presence of storage in very close proximity to smoke detectors can result in a delay in detection, as the free passage of smoke to the detectors is blocked. Materials stored too close to sprinkler heads can impair both the efficiency of detection and the effectiveness of the water discharge.

Finally, bad housekeeping may cause difficulties for the fire brigade. Badly stacked goods, once alight, may present a hazard to firefighters. The presence of clear aisles, however, may make fire brigade operations less difficult when the premises are smoke filled. Moreover, access for fire brigade appliances may be made difficult by poor external storage practices.

Further Reading

1. *Fire Safety Data Sheet MR2: Fire safety planning in industry and commerce*. Fire Protection Association.
2. *Fire Safety Data Sheet MR11: Occupational fire brigades and fire teams: organisation, role and functions*. Fire Protection Association.

Chapter 16

Inspection, Testing and Maintenance

Once fire protection measures have been provided in a building, they must not then be ignored. Fire certificates issued under the Fire Precautions Act may incorporate requirements over ongoing maintenance (see Chapter 1). Fire insurance policies may also incorporate warranties concerning the maintenance of systems, such as sprinklers; failure to do so could threaten the validity of the insurance in the event of fire. Moreover, there is a vast amount of recognised guidance on this subject: it may be relatively simple to prove liability in civil law, for injury or losses suffered by third parties as a result of failures of fire protection measures due to a lack of maintenance.

Formal inspections should be a part of a company's approach to safety. However, a general awareness on the part of all employees, particularly supervisors, engineers and managers, can ensure that, as the building occupants go about their day to day activities, new fire risks are identified and addressed, while deficiencies in fire protection are recognised, reported and rectified.

Formal self inspection procedures will vary in frequency and nature, according to the nature of the premises. The most thorough fire safety inspections, in which every room of the building is inspected, may be incorporated in more wide ranging health and safety inspections. Less detailed inspections, where housekeeping and fire prevention standards are checked and means of escape are inspected, should be carried out on a more frequent basis. The use of checklists can help to ensure that nothing is missed in the course of inspections. These should be tailor-made for the premises. Matters relevant to fire prevention in particular, may vary between one building and another. It is, however, important to ensure that any checklist is used simply as an *aide-mémoire*. The slavish following of a checklist can stifle proper thought regarding problems that may affect fire safety but which do not appear on the checklist.

Routine and formal inspections of any building frequently lead to identification of requirements for the maintenance of passive fire protection measures. Common examples are new service penetrations that have not been properly fire stopped, self-closing devices that require adjustment in order to close fire resisting doors firmly shut in their frames, and gaps around fire resisting doors through which smoke could spread.

In the case of active systems, visual inspection is necessary but not sufficient, and specific test routines are necessary to ensure that the systems will operate on demand. It is essential, therefore, that fire alarm systems, emergency lighting installations, sprinkler water gongs, etc are tested frequently. Active systems and equipment also require periodic inspection, testing, servicing and maintenance by persons with technical knowledge. This will normally require contracts with specialist contractors for periodic visits. In large organisations, there may be suitably trained and experienced persons within the organisation. It is essential in this case, that the in-house persons possess the same skills and qualifications as a typical specialist contractor and that servicing and maintenance routines comply with recognised trade practices.

Reference has been made in previous chapters to specific items that should be checked, and the requirements for servicing and maintaining equipment. Typical frequencies at which certain inspections, tests and maintenance work should be undertaken are listed below. However, in the case of a specific building, the frequencies at which the work shown below should be undertaken should take into account:

(a) the nature of the building and the risk from fire
(b) the recommendations of equipment manufacturers and suppliers
(c) relevant British Standards and other recognised codes of good practice
(d) any requirements or recommendations of the fire authority
(e) any requirements or recommendations of the company's fire insurers.

It should be noted that the periods shown below are the minimum common standard; where a monthly check is recommended, more stringent tests may be required less frequently, eg annually.

Daily

(a) check fire alarm control and indicating equipment and the log book
(b) check the control panels of emergency lighting central batteries or generators, and the log book
(c) ensure that, if applicable, any fastenings are removed from fire exits and that escape routes are unobstructed.

Weekly

(a) check escape routes, final exit doors and general housekeeping
(b) test fire alarm systems
(c) test sprinkler installations.

Monthly

(a) test emergency lighting
(b) check that fire safety signs are in place and visible
(c) check that all fire extinguishers are in position, undamaged, accessible, etc
(d) check hose reels.

Quarterly

(a) maintenance of fire alarm systems
(b) maintenance of sprinkler systems.

Six Monthly

Maintenance of gaseous extinguishing installations.

Annually

Maintenance of fire extinguishing appliances.

Five Yearly

Inspection and test of electrical installation by a qualified person.

Proper records should be kept of all inspections, tests, defects, rectification work and routine maintenance. The keeping of such records may be a requirement of a fire certificate. In the case of, for example, inspections and tests of sprinkler installations, the completion of a record card may be a requirement of the fire insurer. Detailed records should, in any event, be kept in a log book, regardless of whether there is a specific requirement to do so. The existence of such records may provide evidence for defence against prosecution or civil action, in the event of allegations that an occupier has neglected to maintain fire protection measures in proper working order.

Chapter 17

Fire Procedures

A significant factor in multiple fatality fires in non-domestic premises is the incorrect response of building occupants. The behaviour of occupants is sometimes a more important cause of multiple deaths than failures in building design or fire protection equipment. This is particularly true of buildings that satisfy current legislative requirements, especially if no people sleep in the building. These facts underline the need for pre-planned fire procedures and for training of building occupants in the procedures. Staff training is discussed in Chaper 18 of this book; the subject of fire procedures is considered below.

In most buildings, fire procedures need not be complicated, and indeed must not be permitted to become so. The services of a specialist will not normally be required to write the fire procedures for the building. However, it is not possible to define an exact procedure that will apply to every building. Shutting down equipment may be part of the fire procedures in an industrial site whereas, in most office buildings, such actions are less likely to be necessary.

Most fire procedures are written for three groups of occupants:

(a) the person(s) who discovers the fire
(b) persons who hear the fire alarm but have no special duties in the event of fire
(c) persons with special duties to perform when a warning of fire is given.

Action on Discovery of a fire

The simplest fire procedures are those to which the mnemonic RIP applies:

— **R**aise the alarm

— **I**nform the fire brigade
— **P**ut the fire out

In fire procedure notices, these three actions are normally set out in a theoretical chronological order, as though there were only one occupant of the building. This is also the manner in which they are considered below. However, in practice, all three measures need to be implemented simultaneously or as quickly as possible. If there are several occupants in the area of the fire, one person should tackle the fire immediately if it is safe to do so, while a colleague raises the alarm and ensures that the fire brigade are summoned.

Raising the Alarm

The first action should be to warn all occupants of the danger, to avoid any delay in evacuating the building. It should be the recognised right of any person to operate the fire alarm system if they suspect, or know, that there is a fire in the building. Fire procedures based on informing a manager, telephoning a switchboard operator, security officer, fire warden, etc if a fire occurs, are inherently dangerous and divorced from the reality of both fire behaviour and human behaviour. Concerns that the alarm might be raised in the event of only a "small" fire are unlikely to be considered with great sympathy if or when a "large" fire develops.

In some buildings, it may be unnecessary to evacuate the entire building when a fire is discovered and the alarm system is operated. However, the fire alarm system should normally be configured in such a manner that any person who operates a manual call point receives confirmation (normally by operation of the alarm sounders in the area) that the signal has been received at the fire alarm control equipment. Even in buildings with two stage alarms, in which an "alert" signal, rather than an evacuation signal is given in some areas, an immediate evacuation signal should be given in the area in which the manual call point is operated. The arrangement, sometimes found in older fire alarm systems, where, on operation of a manual call point, the whole building (including the area in which the call point is located) is given an "alert" signal, but no one in the area of the fire actually evacuates, is no longer acceptable. At the very least, operation of a manual call point should normally lead to evacuation of those in the area (eg floor of the building) in which the call point is situated.

In some buildings, after operating a manual call point, it may be required that further information is given, by telephone or in person, to a responsible person at a continuously manned location, such as a reception desk or switchboard. The need for this procedure may arise because of the complexity of the building and the need for key staff to be made aware of the circumstances as soon as possible. The use of the telephone is not, however, an acceptable means of actually raising the alarm, and should only be used to give further details after the alarm is sounding.

Informing the fire brigade

It is vital to ensure that the fire brigade are immediately summoned to every outbreak of fire, however small it may be. Operation of a manual call point should, therefore, be regarded as synonymous with the existence of a fire. (This will normally be true also of operation of an automatic fire detector.) As discussed in Chapter 2, fire growth can be very rapid in its early stages, and even a short delay in summoning the fire brigade may put lives at risk and result in additional loss of property. A delay in summoning the fire brigade is a common factor of most fire disasters, such as the Summerland leisure centre fire, the fire at Woolworth's, Manchester, the Stardust discotheque fire in Dublin, and the fire at King's Cross underground station. Action must, therefore, be taken to summon the fire brigade as soon as the fire alarm is actuated.

Responsibility for summoning the fire brigade in the event of fire must be pre-planned. It is desirable that the responsibility is placed on a person other than the person(s) who actually discovers the fire. For example, the procedure may be that, on hearing the fire alarm, the switchboard operator will summon the fire brigade before evacuating the building. Care must be taken to ensure that, due to a failure of the fire alarm system, a situation cannot arise whereby the alarm is sounding, the person who discovers the fire assumes that the brigade will be summoned, but the switchboard operator is unaware of the alarm signal.

The person who is responsible for summoning the fire brigade should be in a position to monitor closely the main fire alarm panel. It can then be assumed that, when an alarm is raised and alarm sounders operate, the signal will be displayed on the main fire alarm panel, and the person who monitors the panel will summon the fire brigade. Problems can arise, however, if the switchboard operator merely monitors a repeat indicator panel, situated in a separate part of the site from the main control panel. A failure in the link to the repeat indicator panel could result in a major delay in the summoning of the fire brigade. The fire procedure should then be that, after raising the alarm, someone contacts the switchboard operator from a place of safety to ensure that the fire brigade have been summoned.

The alarm signal may be relayed to an alarm company monitoring centre (central station), from where the fire brigade will be summoned as soon as the signal is received. Although this should ensure that the fire brigade will be summoned quickly when the alarm system is operated (and some account may then be taken of this in fire procedures), a central station connection never obviates the need for an emergency call to the fire brigade from the premises, if occupied. The link to the central station can fail or, in the case of digital communicators (see Chapter 10), be significantly delayed. Furthermore, it is not unknown for incorrect procedures at the central station to result in a long delay or failure in summoning of the fire brigade.

In buildings that have no suitable and continuously manned location at which the fire alarm control panel is monitored, the responsibility for summoning the fire brigade should still be pre-planned. For example, it may be the duty of a manager or supervisor, but it should be ensured that the duty is not delegated to a named individual (who may not always be present). In smaller premises, or those in which it is not practicable to delegate the duty for summoning the fire brigade, it may be necessary to place the responsibility for summoning the fire brigade on the person who discovers the fire. In this case, the duty should be made clear in the written fire procedures. Even in buildings with switchboard operators or reception desks, it may be necessary to resort to less formal, but clearly documented, procedures for summoning the fire brigade outside normal working hours.

Although immediate summoning of the fire brigade has been stressed, occupants should not place themselves at risk to make the call. It may be necessary to retreat to a safe area of the building or to another building. However, procedures should never require the use of a telephone on a higher floor level than the fire, from which escape might prove difficult (except in the case of basements).

Extinguishing the fire

Procedures must not require persons to attempt to extinguish a fire, but should suggest that extinguishing action may be taken if it is safe to do so. The use of extinguishing appliances by occupants is a rather contentious subject (see Chapter 11) but, in practice, it is entirely unrealistic to have a procedure whereby even the smallest fire is left to burn for, perhaps, ten minutes or more, pending the arrival of the fire brigade. Extinguishing action should, however, generally be implemented only in tandem with raising the alarm and summoning the fire brigade.

Action on Hearing the Fire Alarm

The correct action on hearing the fire alarm sound depends on whether an alert signal or an evacuation signal is being given. In buildings with single stage evacuation arrangements, only the evacuation signal will ever occur. In buildings with staged evacuation arrangements (eg two stage or phased evacuation), an evacuation signal will be given in the area of the fire, and an alert signal will be given in other areas.

On hearing an alert signal, occupants should prepare for a possible evacuation. The form of preparation will vary from one building to another. In some buildings, equipment might be shut down during the alert stage. It is also wise to begin evacuation of disabled people at the alert stage.

The evacuation signal must be regarded as an instruction to occupants to evacuate immediately. There must be no delays while belongings are collected, an item on the agenda of a meeting is finished, telephone calls are finished, or meals in a restaurant are paid for or eaten. However, any equipment that might itself create a fire hazard if left unattended, should be switched off. As occupants make their escape, all doors should be closed, particularly those designated as fire doors. If it is possible to close windows quickly, this may also be appropriate, but is less essential.

All occupants, on evacuation, should report to a pre-determined assembly point for a roll call. Re-entry of the building should be strictly prohibited until the fire brigade officer in charge declares that it is safe to do so. In particular, the silencing of the fire alarm should never be regarded as an indication that it is safe to re-enter the building; the signal may have been silenced deliberately because it is known that the building is evacuated, or the fire may have damaged the alarm system, causing it to stop sounding.

Special Duties

Summoning the Fire Brigade

The summoning of the fire brigade may be the responsibility of a designated post (but not named individual), such as a switchboard operator. In this case, a special procedure should be formulated for the person in question. Although this may seem trivial as the procedure will normally be a matter of dialling 999, asking for the fire brigade and requesting their attendance at the premises, some of the detail of these simple actions benefits from pre-planning.

The procedure should include the exact manner in which the address of the premises should be given to the fire brigade. This will avoid any confusion or error in communication by, for example, using local terminology to a centralised fire control operator who receives fire calls from an entire county.

As there are only 67 fire brigades in the United Kingdom, the area served by any control room is very large. Local descriptions of premises, such as "Ashmores" or "the bakers in the High Street" may mean nothing to a fire control operator many miles away. Virtually all fire brigade controls are computerised, and presentation of an address in a manner that the computer can recognise enables efficient response by the fire brigade. In case of doubt, the relevant fire brigade can advise on the manner in which an address should be presented. The information should include:

(a) the name of the company
(b) the correct postal address, including the area or district and the town
(c) the telephone number
(d) brief circumstances, such as automatic fire alarm actuating, fire in canteen, etc
(e) in the case of complex buildings or sites, the appropriate entrance which the fire brigade should use.

Fire Wardens

In larger buildings, or those in which a roll call after evacuation is ineffective due to a varying occupancy or the presence of members of the public, designated fire wardens and nominated deputies, should be appointed for each area of the building. In the event of fire, the fire wardens should be responsible for ensuring that their areas are evacuated. They should then evacuate and report that their area (including any toilets) is clear to the person in charge at the assembly point.

It should be stressed that no one in a building should delay their evacuation pending instructions from a fire warden. The absence of fire wardens should have no effect on the evacuation, but could affect the reliability and value of information that is available to the fire brigade. A well conducted evacuation should enable the fire brigade to turn their attention to firefighting, rather than searching for non-existent occupants.

If a fire warden scheme is operated, provisions must be made for fire wardens to be present at all times. Normally, fire wardens are named persons, but there must be sufficient wardens and deputies to cater for absences. The problem of absences can be avoided by incorporating the duties of fire warden with a designated post, such as shift supervisor, which it is known must always be filled. This, however, suffers from the possible disadvantage that an individual post holder may not be interested in the duties of fire warden, have inadequate time or desire to attend fire warden's training sessions, and generally be reluctant to take the duty seriously.

Roll Call

A responsible person(s) should be designated to account for occupants at the evacuation assembly point(s). This person must obviously have available a list of occupants who should be present at the time of the evacuation. Information regarding the status of the evacuation, and any person for whom it is impossible to account, should be given to the fire brigade on their arrival.

Reception of the Fire Brigade

An appropriate person should be made responsible for meeting the fire brigade on arrival and liaising with the officer in charge. The person should be familiar with the building and be in a position to advise regarding the location of any information packs for the fire brigade, the layout of the building, fire protection measures, building services and their controls, etc. This may require the availability of other persons, such as the building services engineer, who can provide specialist information if it is needed by the fire brigade.

Security Guards

Security guards may be given special duties to perform in the event of fire. In a building with particular security risks, these duties may relate to the primary role of the guards. However, security personnel may be required to perform other duties, such as:

- grounding lifts to ensure that they are not used to evacuate (except in the case of disabled people who may use special evacuation lifts (see Chapter 6)
- acting as lift operators for any evacuation lifts
- preventing persons from entering the building, until a general re-occupation is permitted
- co-ordinating salvage work
- providing advice to the fire brigade concerning the building.

Senior Management

A senior manager should be in overall charge until the fire brigade arrives. It should be understood that, on arrival, the fire brigade will take charge. However, the manager should be in a position to make decisions regarding alternative accommodation for building occupants, notification or call out of other managers or specialist employees, implementation of contingency plans, etc.

Further Reading

1. *Fire Safety Data Sheet MR7: Procedure in event of fire.* Fire Protection Association.

Chapter 18

Staff Training and Fire Drills

Staff training and fire drills are clearly related but are not synonymous. Yet it is a common misconception that a company's training obligations are satisfied by carrying out periodic fire drills. Fire drills are both necessary and useful, but they do not educate employees in all matters with which they should be familiar.

Training of staff in fire safety matters remains a contentious issue, however, with many companies taking the view that it is not reasonably practicable to provide training for all employees. This view has probably never been fully tested in court but, the fact that certain companies take the matter of fire training very seriously, and are able to train a large number of employees, adequately demonstrates the feasibility of providing proper training for all employees.

Prosecutions relating to fire safety training in isolation appear to be relatively rare, although failure to provide staff training is sometimes a matter for which companies are prosecuted, along with a host of other offences, when enforcing authorities decide to act because of an organisation's gross failure to comply with the law.

Legal Requirements for Training

Section 2 of the Health and Safety at Work, etc Act 1974 imposes a general duty on employers to provide instruction and training to ensure, as far as reasonably practicable, the health and safety at work of employees. As discussed in the previous chapter, there is ample evidence that incorrect response by occupants is usually a major contributory factor in most fire disasters. Also, research that has been undertaken on human behaviour in fire is now so extensive that an absence of fire training does not appear to be consistent with the requirements of the Act.

Section 6 of the Fire Precautions Act 1971 empowers (but does not actually require) the fire authority to impose such requirements as the fire authority consider appropriate in the circumstances to ensure that

> persons employed to work in the premises receive appropriate instruction or training in what to do in case of fire, and that records are kept of instruction or training given for that purpose.

Guidance contained in the "Guide to fire precautions in existing places of work that require a fire certificate", recommends that instruction should be given by a competent person to ensure that everyone at work is instructed preferably twice, but at least once, every year. It is this requirement that is normally incorporated in a fire certificate, thereby making training mandatory. Such is the importance of training that, as discussed in Chapter 1, instruction of employees in what to do in case of fire is one of the three "interim duties" imposed by the Fire Precautions Act (as amended), pending response by a fire authority to an application for a fire certificate.

Method of Training

Initial training should be given as part of any induction course for new employees. If this is not within a very short time of joining the company, new employees should be given basic instruction concerning escape routes, fire procedures, fire alarm signals, etc on the day they begin work in the building. At the very least, they should initially be given a tour of all escape routes, including any alternative routes that do not form part of the normal access routes. If employees do not attend a formal induction course, they should be given detailed instruction on fire matters as soon as possible after joining the company. Instruction should be based on written material, which is given to the employee, but should always, in addition, comprise verbal instruction. Standard fire instruction leaflets are not adequate; the instructions should be tailor-made for the building in question.

Instruction should be given to all persons who work in the building. This includes permanent shift workers (eg night shift security staff), part-time staff, cleaners, etc. Special training may be necessary for those with particular duties, such as fire wardens. After initial training on joining the organisation, employees should receive refresher training once or twice a year.

Some organisations consider fire training to be impracticable as they believe employees need to be sent off on an external course. Such courses may be one method for training those with special duties, but are not normally necessary for all building occupants. After the initial induction training, which may be part of an induction course or merely a briefing from someone with adequate knowledge, short sessions can be held periodically by the company fire officer, safety officer or other suitably knowledgeable person. Various external organisations, including consultants, the Fire Protection Association and some fire brigades, can also provide such training on the premises.

Refresher training should not be time consuming. In some companies, it may involve no more than a thirty-minute session. These training sessions should not merely reiterate the standard fire instructions for the building. The objective should be to raise the awareness of employees by attracting their attention and providing material that is of interest. Videos can be of assistance, and numerous useful videos dealing with different aspects of fire safety can be purchased or hired. Refresher training also offers an opportunity to discuss any fire problems that have arisen in the company, or causes of false alarms that have occurred. Interest can also be generated by imparting guidance on domestic fire safety matters for the employees' own benefit.

Content of Training Sessions

The matters discussed below should be covered in all training sessions. To these, should be added other matters that are more specific to the premises, such as particular fire prevention practices, smoking policies, and fire precautions relevant to particular equipment or processes.

Means of Escape

All employees must be made familiar with all means of escape from the building in which they work. It is particularly important that they are made aware of escape routes that are different from the normal entrances and exits. Employees should also be shown how to operate any exit devices, such as panic bars.

Action in the Event of Fire

All employees should be instructed in the actions to take in the event of fire. This should include any special duties, such as those allocated to fire wardens. Procedures for evacuation of disabled people should also be outlined.

Means of Raising the Alarm

All employees must be familiar with the means of raising the alarm, which normally involves the operation of a manual call point. There is some variation between one type of call point and another—particularly older types, in which the glass breaks into fragments, and modern types in which it does not. The exact method of operating the type of call point that is present in the building should, therefore, be demonstrated. A member of staff should be given the opportunity to operate a call point on each occasion that a fire drill is held (see below). Employees should also be reminded of the locations of manual call points

Means of Summoning the Fire Brigade

The need for the fire brigade to be summoned to all fires should be stressed in training sessions. The 999 emergency call procedure should be explained. Many people do not realise that the first person they will speak to is the British Telecom or Mercury operator, who will only wish to know which emergency service is required. People commonly forget that they are not talking to the fire brigade at this stage, and begin to describe the circumstances of the fire. If the duty of summoning the fire brigade is associated with a specific post, such as a receptionist, consideration might be given to permitting a 999 call to be made, by prior arrangement with British Telecom or Mercury and the fire brigade, at the time of a fire drill.

Action on Hearing the Fire Brigade

One of the most important points to stress during training sessions is that occupants must evacuate as soon as the evacuation signal is given. People are always reluctant to do so; they tend to assume that the signal is the result of a false alarm and do not wish to appear foolish by evacuationg when, perhaps, others are reluctant to do so. This reluctance can be helped by making it clear that management will support an evacuation even if a false alarm has occurred, and by using visual aids that demonstrate the speed with which fire can develop. It is necessary to create an appreciation of the hazard that fire presents to life.

If evacuation times are to be minimised, it must be stressed to employees that all means of escape should be used, including those that are not part of the normal access routes and which require the use of exit devices. It should also be emphasised that lifts must not be used.

Location and Use of Fire Appliances

All employees must know the location of the nearest fire appliances to their normal working location and the general layout of appliances in the building. This can prevent undue delay in tackling a small fire which might otherwise grow to untenable proportions, while people search for a fire extinguisher.

Employees must understand the colour coding of portable extinguishers, and the types of fire for which the extinguishers provided in the building are suitable. The method of operation of extinguishers and hose reels should also be demonstrated. Ideally, selected members of staff should be permitted to discharge extinguishers onto fires so that they obtain an appreciation of the extinguisher's capability. This may not always be possible without transporting employees to a separate location. However, this more in-depth training should be considered for security guards, fire wardens and those responsible for giving instruction to others.

If use on fires is not possible, staff should still be permitted to discharge extinguishers in, for example, an open yard or loading bay, merely to reinforce the method of operation and particular problems, such as the noise of discharge and the chilling of the horn of CO_2 extinguishers. Halon extinguishers should not, however, be discharged in view of the effect of halon on the ozone layer. Where any type of extinguisher cannot actually be discharged in training sessions, a sample of the extinguisher should be shown to employees, its method of operation should be described, and a film of an actual discharge should be shown.

General Fire Precautions

Occupants of a building often negate the fire precautions in the building simply because they do not understand the function of smoke stop or fire resisting doors, which they wedge open, or the need to keep escape routes clear of combustible materials. It is important that they are not only instructed on these mandatory measures but also on the reasons for them. In some buildings, there may be special precautions to take because of hazardous activities or materials and, again, it is vital that staff are aware of the appropriate precautions.

Fire Drills

Fire drills are a useful means of reinforcing evacuation procedures and monitoring their effectiveness. Fire certificates normally require fire drills to be carried out either once or twice a year. Sometimes, requirements concerning the timing of drills (eg at least one drill per annum for night shift workers) are specified.

Fire drills are not always taken seriously by employees or managers, and are seen as an unnecessary interruption to business. This is unfortunate as a properly conducted drill can highlight problems such as the failure of occupants to use all fire exits resulting in an inordinately long evacuation time.

The evacuation time, defined as the time between the operation of the alarm and the evacuation of the last person from the building, should always be measured and recorded. In premises with more than one staircase or fire exit, the use of one staircase or exit should be prohibited, so that occupants are forced to use alternative routes. The design of buildings is such that acceptable evacuation times should still be physically possible. The drill should begin by permitting an employee to operate a manual call point. All occupants, including senior management and disabled people, should participate in the drill. Exemptions should be rare and should only be given in very exceptional circumstances, to persons on whose presence a critical continuous operation absolutely depends.

A "post mortem" should always be held soon after each drill. This provides an opportunity for fire wardens to report problems, any unwillingness to evacuate by specific groups, difficulties in hearing the alarm system, etc.

Further Reading

1. *Fire Safety Data Sheet MR9: First day induction training*. Fire Protection Association
2. *Fire Safety Data Sheet MR10: Fire safety training*. Fire Protection Association.
3. Fire Safety Data Sheet MR12: *Fire safety education and training of people at work*. Fire Protection Association.

Appendix A
Glossary of Terms

The following definitions are generally in accordance with either BS 4422 (Glossary of terms associated with fire) or with particular British Standards relating to the topic in question. Some definitions have been modified, or new definitions have been formulated, to coincide with the context in which the terms are used in this book.

addressable fire alarm system See Fire alarm system, addressable.
AFFF Aqueous film forming foam. The concentrate contains perfluorosurfactants which, when added to water at between 1% and 3%, cause a marked reduction in surface tension.
alternate sprinkler system See **automatic sprinkler system,** alternate.
alternative escape routes Escape routes sufficiently separated by either direction and space, or by fire resisting construction, to ensure that one is still available should the other be affected by fire.
analogue detector See **fire detector**, analogue.
arson Fire originated by malicious intent.
aspirating fire detection system A fire detection system in which a sample of the atmosphere in the protected space is sucked by a fan or pump into a detector which may be remote from the protected space.
assumed maximum area of operation (AMAO) of a sprinkler system The maximum area over which it is assumed, for design purposes, that sprinklers will operate in a fire.
auto-dialler A device that transmits a fire alarm warning to a remote centre by establishing communications via a switched telephone network.
auto-ignition temperature The minimum temperature at which a material will ignite spontaneously under specified test conditions.
automatic fire alarm system A fire alarm system in which the alarm of fire can be initiated automatically by fire detectors.
automatic release mechanism A device that may be used for holding

a door in the open position, against the action of a door closer, and automatically releasing under specified conditions.

automatic sprinkler system A system of water pipes fitted with sprinkler heads at suitable intervals and heights and designed to control or extinguish a fire by the discharge of water, in which each of the heads opens automatically at a specified temperature.

automatic sprinkler system, alternate An automatic sprinkler system in which the pipes may optionally be charged with air or water.

automatic sprinkler system, dry pipe An automatic sprinkler system in which the pipes are normally charged with air to avoid the risk of water freezing in the pipes.

automatic sprinkler system, pre-action A dry pipe automatic sprinkler system in which operation of an associated automatic fire alarm system results in the flow of water into the sprinkler pipework.

automatic sprinkler system, wet pipe An automatic sprinkler system in which the pipes are constantly charged with water.

beam detector The components, including any reflectors, necessary for the detection of smoke by the attentuation of an optical beam. (Beam detectors may also respond to heat by detection of thermal turbulence.)

cavity barrier A construction provided to close a concealed space against penetration of smoke or flame, or provided to restrict the movement of smoke or flame within such a space.

central battery emergency lighting A system of emergency lighting in which all the luminaires are powered from a central battery.

central station A continuously manned remote centre in which the information concerning the state of alarm systems is displayed and/or recorded.

Class A fire A fire involving solid materials, usually of an organic nature, in which combustion normally takes place with the formation of glowing embers.

Class B fire A fire involving liquids or liquefiable solids.

Class C fire A fire involving a gas or gases.

Class D fire A fire involving metals.

compartmentation The sub-division of a building by fire resisting walls and/or floors for the purpose of limiting fire spread within the building.

compartment floor A fire resisting floor used in the separation of one fire compartment from another.

compartment wall A fire resisting wall used in the separation of one fire compartment from another.

consequential loss (also known as business interruption) Loss of revenue during the period of interruption of a business which follows destruction or damage by fire.

control and indicating equipment See **Fire alarm control and indicating equipment**.

dead end An area from which escape is possible in one direction only.

designated use (under the Fire Precautions Act 1971) Use of premises for a purpose to which the Fire Precautions Act applies by virtue of a Designating Order issued by the Secretary of State.

digital communicator Signalling equipment that automatically transmits information on the state of an alarm system to an interacting receiver unit in a remote centre via a switched telephone network using a form of coded transmission.

direct distance The shortest distance from any point within the floor area, measured within the external enclosures of the building, to the nearest storey exit, ignoring walls, partitions and fittings, other than the enclosing walls/partitions to protected stairways.

distribution pipe A sprinkler pipe which feeds either a range pipe directly or a single sprinkler on a non-terminal range pipe more than 300mm long.

drencher system A system used to distribute water over a surface to provide protection against fire exposure.

dry rising main (dry riser) A vertical pipe installed in a building for fire fighting purposes, fitted with inlet connections at the fire brigade access level and landing valves at specified points, which is normally dry but is capable of being charged with water, usually by pumping from fire service appliances.

dry sprinkler system See **automatic sprinkler system, dry pipe**.

emergency lighting Lighting provided for use when the supply to the normal lighting fails.

escape lighting That part of the emergency lighting which is provided to ensure that the escape route is illuminated at all material times.

estimated maximum loss (EML) The maximum loss that might reasonably be anticipated from a fire in the premises. (Differing insurance companies vary in their exact definition of this term. Some take active and passive fire protection into account.)

evacuation lift A lift that may be used for the evacuation of disabled people in a fire.

false alarm A signal from a fire alarm system that arises from a cause other than a fire in the premises protected by the fire alarm system.

final exit The termination of an escape route from a building, giving direct access to a street, passageway, walkway or open space.

fire alarm control equipment Equipment which, on receipt of a fire signal, controls the giving of a fire alarm by one or more of the following:

(a) fire alarm sounders
(b) fire alarm indicating equipment
(c) transmitting a signal to other fire alarm control equipment.

fire alarm control and indicating equipment A combination of fire alarm control equipment and fire alarm indicating equipment.

fire alarm indicating equipment The part of a fire alarm system located at protected premises which provides indication of any fire alarm or fault warning signal received from fire alarm control equipment.

fire alarm sounder A component of a fire alarm system for giving an audible warning of fire.

fire alarm system, addressable A fire alarm system in which signals from each detector and/or call point are individually identified at the control panel.

fire alarm zone A sub-division of the protected premises such that the occurrence of a fire within it will be indicated by a fire alarm system separately from an indication of fire in any other sub-division.

fire break door, shutter, floor or wall A fire resisting element that is designed to comply with the relevant rules of the Loss Prevention Council.

fire compartment A building or part of a building, comprising one or more rooms, spaces or storeys, constructed to prevent the spread of fire to or from another part of the same building, or an adjoining building.

fire damper A damper which is designed to prevent the passage of fire.

fire detector A part of an automatic fire alarm system that contains at least one sensor which constantly, or at frequent intervals, monitors at least one suitable physical and/or chemical phenomenon associated with fire, and that provides at least one corresponding signal to the control and indicating equipment.

fire detector, analogue A fire detector which gives an output signal representing the value of the sensed phenomenon. This detector does not itself make a decision of fire.

fire detector, flame (radiation) A form of fire detector which responds to radiation emitted by a fire.

fire detector, heat A form of fire detector which responds to an increase in temperature. The response may occur only at a fixed temperature (fixed temperature heat detector) or when the temperature rises at a sufficient rate (rate-of-rise heat detector) or both.

fire detector, line type A form of fire detector which responds to the phenomenon detected anywhere along its length.

fire detector, multi-state A fire detector which gives one of a limited number (greater than two) output states relating to "normal" or "fire alarm" and other abnormal conditions.

fire detector, point type A form of fire detector which responds to the phenomenon detected at a fixed point.

fire detector, smoke A form of fire detector which responds to particulate combustion products suspended in the atmosphere.

fire detector, two-state A fire detector which gives one of two output states relating to either "normal" or "fire alarm" conditions.

fire drill (evacuation drill) Rehearsal of the evacuation procedure involving participation of the occupants of the premises.

fire equipment sign A safety sign that indicates the location of the fire fighting equipment and/or how it should be used.

fire extinguisher A portable item of fire fighting equipment containing a fire extinguishing medium which is expelled by internal pressure.

firefighting lift A lift designated to have additional protection, with controls that enable it to be used under the direct control of the fire brigade in fighting a fire.

firefighting lift switch A switch provided to enable the fire service to obtain immediate control of a firefighting lift. Operation of a firefighting lift switch returns the firefighting lift to the fire service access level and affects the way in which the lift control system operates.

firefighting lobby A protected lobby for providing access from a firefighting stairway to the accommodation area and to any associated firefighting lift.

firefighting shaft A protected shaft containing a firefighting stairway, firefighting lobbies and, if provided, a firefighting lift.

firefighting stairway A protected stairway communicating with the accommodation area only through a firefighting lobby.

fire load The calorific energy of the entire contents of a space, including the facings of the walls, partitions, floors and ceilings.

fire main A water supply pipe, fitted with landing valves at specified points, installed in a building for firefighting purposes.

fireman's emergency switch A switch provided for emergency isolation of certain electrical equipment.

fire prevention Measures to prevent the outbreak of a fire.

fire protection Design features, systems, equipment, buildings, or other structures to reduce danger to persons and property by detecting, extinguishing or containing fires.

fire protection, active Fire protection measures that change state when fire occurs, so that the post-fire condition of the protective measure is different from the pre-fire condition.

fire protection, passive Fire protection measures that need not change in any manner in order to perform their fire protection function.

fire resistance The ability of an element of building construction, component or structure to fulfil, for a stated period of time, the required stability, fire integrity and/or thermal insulation and/or other expected duty in a standard fire resistance test.

fire safety sign A sign that gives a message about fire safety by a combination of geometric form, safety colour and symbol or text or both.

fire stop A seal provided to close an imperfection of fit or design tolerance between elements or components, to restrict or prevent the passage of fire and smoke.

fire telephone A telephone provided for emergency communication within the building in the event of fire.

fire warden An individual charged with specific responsibilities in the event of fire, normally involving a check to ensure that a particular area of the building has been evacuated.

fixed fire extinguishing system A system of fixed fire protection equipment for discharging a fire extinguishing or suppressing medium or media.

flammability limits The minimum and maximum concentration of vapour-to-air below and above which propagation of a flame will not occur in the presence of an ignition source.

flashover A sudden transition to a state of total surface involvement in a fire of combustible materials within a compartment.

flashpoint The temperature at which the vapour pressure of a flammable liquid is sufficiently high to permit the formation of a vapour/air mixture at the surface which is just within the lower limit of flammability. The application of an ignition source will then cause a pre-mixed flame to propagate through the mixture.

foam extinguishing system A system of pipes connected to a supply of foam and fitted with nozzles at suitable intervals and heights, through which foam is discharged.

foam inlet Fixed equipment consisting of an inlet connection, fixed piping and a discharge assembly, enabling firemen to introduce foam into an enclosed compartment.

foam system, high expansion A foam system which produces foam with an expansion ratio (the ratio of the volume of foam to the volume of foam solution from which it was made) between 201 and 1000.

foam system, low expansion A foam system which produces foam with an expansion ratio (the ratio of the volume of foam to the volume of foam solution from which it was made) not exceeding 20.

foam system, medium expansion A foam system which produces foam with an expansion ratio (the ratio of the volume of foam to the volume of foam solution from which it was made) between 21 and 200.

fusible link A soldered connecting link designed to part on melting at a specified temperature.

halon A halogenated hydrocarbon normally used as a fire extinguishing agent.

halon extinguishing system, central bank A fixed extinguishing system in which the extinguishing agent is halon and is stored in a central bank of storage containers from which distribution pipework leads to the protected space via a manifold.

halon extinguishing system, modular A fixed extinguishing system in which the agent is halon and is stored in individual containers, usually each having a single nozzle outlet, distributed throughout the protected space.

hazard category (of a sprinkler installation) A sprinkler system design parameter that takes into account the size of fire and rapidity of fire development that might be expected in the type of occupancy in which the system is installed.

hazardous area (in relation to flammable gases, vapours and mists) An area in which explosive atmospheres are, or may be expected to be, present in quantities such as to require special precautions for the construction and use of electrical apparatus.

hazardous area, zone 0 A hazardous area in which an explosive atmosphere is continuously present, or present for long periods.

hazardous area, zone 1 A hazardous area in which an explosive atmosphere is likely to occur in normal operation.

hazardous area, zone 2 A hazardous area in which an explosive atmosphere is not likely to occur in normal operation, and if it occurs will exist for only a short time.

improvement notice (under the Fire Precautions Act 1971) A legally binding notice served by the fire authority on the owner or occupier of a building for which a fire certificate is not required, under s 9D of the Fire Precautions Act, specifying the measures that must be taken in order to bring the premises to the required standard of fire safety.

infra red flame detector A flame detector which responds to infra red radiation.

inner room A room from which escape is possible only by passing through an (access) room.

insulation The ability of a specimen of a separating element to restrict the temperature rise of the unexposed face to below specified levels.

integrity The ability of a specimen of a separating element to contain a fire to specified criteria for collapse, freedom from holes, cracks and fissures and sustained flaming on the unexposed face.

interim duties (under the Fire Precautions Act 1971) Duties imposed on the owner or occupier of a building after an application has been made for a fire certificate, but pending disposal of the application by the fire authority.

intumescent material A material which, when heated, swells to form an insulating char that is able to restrict the egress of hot gases between adjacent surfaces, thus contributing to the integrity of the assembly.

ionisation chamber smoke detector A smoke detector which responds when smoke, having entered the detector, causes a change in ionisation currents within the detector.

landing valve An assembly comprising a valve and outlet connection from a wet or dry rising main.

line detector See **fire detector, line type**.

loadbearing capacity The ability of a specimen of a loadbearing element to support its test load, where appropriate, without exceeding specified criteria with respect to either the extent of, or rate of, deformation or both.

local act An act of Parliament which contains regulations that apply only in a specified geographical area of the country.

local application extinguishing system A fixed fire extinguishing system in which a supply of extinguishing agent is permanently connected to fixed piping with nozzles arranged to discharge the agent directly onto a fire occurring in a defined area that has no enclosure surrounding it, or is only partially enclosed, and that does not produce an extinguishing concentration throughout the entire volume containing the hazard.

maintained emergency lighting A lighting system in which all emergency lighting lamps are in operation at all material times.

mandatory sign A safety sign that indicates that a specific course of action is to be taken.

manual call point A device for the manual operation of an electrical fire alarm system.

manual fire alarm system A fire alarm system that contains no automatic fire detectors and in which an alarm of fire may only be initiated manually.

material alteration An alteration that changes (usually lowering) the standard of fire protection originally required by particular legislation, such as the Fire Precautions Act or the Building Regulations.

means of escape Structural means whereby a safe route is provided for persons to travel from any point in a building to a place of safety without outside assistance.

mimic diagram A topographic representation of the protected premises and their sub-divisions, carrying indicator devices for each sub-division such that the indications of the fire alarm system can be rapidly related to the layout of the premises.

multi-state fire detector See **fire detector, multi-state**.

non-maintained emergency lighting A lighting system in which all emergency lighting lamps are in operation only when the supply to the normal lighting fails.

notice of steps to be taken (under the Fire Precautions Act 1971) A legally binding notice served by a fire authority on an owner or occupier in pursuance of s 5(4) of the Fire Precautions Act requiring improvements in fire precautions as a condition for the issue of a fire certificate.

optical smoke detector A form of fire detector having a photo-electric cell which responds when light is absorbed or scattered by smoke particles.

panic bolt, single A mechanism consisting of a minimum of two sliding bolt heads that engage with keepers in the surrounding door frame or floor for securing a door when closed. The mechanism can be released by hand or body pressure on a bar positioned horizontally across the inside face of the door.

panic latch A mechanism for securing a door when closed. The latch bolt can be released by hand or body pressure on a bar positioned horizontally across the inside face of the door.

phased evacuation A system of evacuation in which different parts of the premises are evacuated in a controlled sequence of phases, those parts of the premises expected to be at greatest risk being evacuated first.

point detector See **fire detector, point type**.

powder An extinguishing medium consisting of finely ground chemicals comprising a main constituent as well as additives to improve its flow, storage and water repellent characteristics.

powder extinguishing system A system of pipes connected to a supply of powder and fitted with nozzles at suitable intervals and heights, through which powder is discharged.

pre-action sprinkler system See **automatic sprinkler system, pre-action**.

pre-alarm warning (pre-warning) An early warning given by a fire alarm system to indicate conditions which might (or might not) represent a fire. Such warnings do not initiate a full fire alarm, but may be used to alert personnel to the need for an inspection, thus reducing the number of false alarms and possibly giving earlier fire action.

pressurisation The establishment of a pressure difference across a barrier to protect a stairway, lobby, escape route or room of a building from smoke penetration.

prohibition notice (under the Fire Precautions Act 1971) A legally binding notice served by a fire authority on the owner or occupier of a building prohibiting or restricting the use of the premises due to the serious risk to persons in the event of fire.

prohibition sign A safety sign that indicates that certain behaviour is prohibited.

protected area (eg protected route, staircase, corridor, lobby, etc)

An area separated from other areas of the building by fire resisting construction.

range pipe A sprinkler pipe which feeds sprinklers directly or via arm pipes of restricted length.

refuge An area that is both separated from a fire by fire resisting construction and provided with a safe route to a storey exit, thus constituting a temporarily safe space for disabled persons to await assistance for their evacuation.

residual current device A device for breaking a circuit automatically when the residual ("out of balance") current exceeds a predetermined amount.

safe condition sign A safety sign that provides information about safe conditions.

satellite A remote centre, normally unmanned, in which the information concerning the state of alarm systems is collected for onward transmission, either direct, or via a further satellite, to a central station.

self contained emergency luminaire A luminaire providing maintained or non-maintained emergency lighting in which all the elements, such as the battery, the lamp, the control unit and the test and monitoring facilities, where provided, are contained within the luminaire or adjacent to it (within one metre).

self luminous sign A type of sign which is self-energised in respect of luminosity and requires no external source of power.

separating wall A compartment wall which separates adjoining buildings.

slave luminaire A luminaire supplied from a central emergency power source and not having its own internal secondary supply.

smoke alarm A device containing within one housing all the components, except possibly the energy source, necessary for detecting fire and giving an audible alarm.

smoke control Measures to control the spread or movement of smoke and combustion gases during a fire within a building.

smoke damper A moveable device for smoke control, open or closed in its normal position, which is automatically or manually actuated

smoke detector See **fire detector, smoke**.

smoke detector, beam type See **beam detector**.

smoke detector, ionisation See **ionisation chamber smoke detector**.

smoke detector, optical See **optical smoke detector**.

smoke seal A seal fitted to a doorset in order to prevent the passage of smoke.

smoke shaft A shaft provided to remove smoke in the event of fire.

smoke vent An opening in the enclosing walls or roof of a building, intended to release heat and smoke in the event of fire, automatically or manually opened.

sounder See **fire alarm sounder**.

spontaneous combustion Combustion that initiates due to self heating of a material without the presence of an external source of ignition.

sprinkler head A temperature sensitive sealing device, which opens to discharge water.

sprinkler head, concealed A recessed sprinkler with a cover plate that disengages when heat is applied.

sprinkler head, conventional pattern A sprinkler that gives a spherical pattern of water discharge.

sprinkler head, flush pattern A pendent sprinkler for fitting partly above the lower plane of the ceiling, but with the temperature sensitive element below the ceiling.

sprinkler head, recessed A sprinkler in which all or part of the heat sensing element is above the plane of the ceiling.

sprinkler head, sidewall pattern A sprinkler that gives on outward half paraboloid discharge.

sprinkler head, spray pattern A sprinkler that gives a downward paraboloid pattern discharge.

sprinkler stop valve The principle control of a sprinkler installation which, when closed, shuts off all supply of water to the installation.

sprinkler system See **automatic sprinkler system**.

standby lighting That part of emergency lighting which may be provided to enable normal activities to continue.

statutory bar (under the Fire Precautions Act 1971) A restriction imposed by Section 13 of the Fire Precautions Act, which restricts the fire authority from making issue of a fire certificate conditional on the provision of structural or other alterations relating to means of escape if the Building Regulations imposed requirements on means of escape at the time of erection of the building, and building plans were deposited with a local authority.

structural fire protection Those features in layout and/or construction which are intended to reduce the effects of a fire.

supplementary sign A sign with text only that may be used in conjunction with a safety sign in order to provide additional information.

sustained emergency luminaire An emergency lighting luminaire containing at least two lamps, one of which is energised from the normal lighting supply and the other from an emergency lighting supply. Such a luminaire is intended to sustain illumination at all material times.

time related fire alarm system A fire alarm system in which the performance of the system, or response to fire conditions, varies according to the time of day or day of week, etc.

total flooding extinguishing system A fixed fire extinguishing system in which a fixed supply of extinguishing agent is permanently connected to fixed piping with nozzles arranged to discharge the agent into an enclosed space in order to produce a concentration sufficient to extinguish fire throughout the entire volume of the enclosed space.

trade off A reduction in the level of one fire protection component while increasing the level of another in order to maintain the same standard of fire protection overall.

travel distance The distance to be travelled from any point in a building, to a protected escape route, external escape route or final exit.

two-stage alarm system A fire alarm system in which the initial evacuation alarm is given only in a restricted part of the premises, with an alert signal being given in the remainder of the premises.

two-state fire detector See Fire detector, two-state.

ultra violet flame detector A flame detector which responds to ultra violet radiation.

unit of exit width Minimum width required for a single file of persons to pass through an exit (generally considered to be 525mm).

warning sign A safety sign that gives warning of a hazard.

water spray system, high velocity A water based extinguishing system in which open nozzles provide a downward discharge of relatively large droplets for the purpose of extinguishing fires in high flashpoint liquids.

water spray system, medium velocity A water based extinguishing system in which sealed or opened sprayers provide a downward discharge of relatively fine water droplets for the purpose of controlling fires in relatively low flashpoint liquids or cooling surfaces.

wet rising main (wet riser) A vertical pipe installed in a building for fire fighting purposes and permanently charged with water from a pressurised supply, fitted with landing valves at specified points.

wet sprinkler system See **automatic sprinkler system, wet pipe**.
zone, fire alarm See **fire alarm zone**.

Further reading

BS 4422: Glossary of terms associated with fire.

Appendix B

Sources of Further Information

Association of Builders' Hardware Manufacturers (ABHM)
Heath Street
Tamworth
Staffs B79 7JH
Tel: 0827 52337

British Approvals for Fire Equipment (BAFE)
48a Eden Street
Kingston upon Thames
Surrey KT1 1EE
Tel: 081-541 1950

British Automatic Sprinkler Association (BASA)
Carlisle House
235–237 Vauxhall Bridge Road
London SW1V 1EJ
Tel: 071-233 7022

British Fire Protection Systems Association (BFPSA)
48a Eden Street
Kingston upon Thames
Surrey KT1 1EE
Tel: 081-459 5855

British Standards Institution (BSI)
2 Park Street
London W1A 2BS
Enquiries: 0908 221166
Orders: 0908 220022

The Chemical Industries Association
The Kings Buildings
Smith Square
London SW1P 3JJ
Tel: 071-834 3399

Confederation for the Registration of Gas Installers (CORGI)
St Martin's House
140 Tottenham Court Road
London W1P 9LN
Tel: 071-387 9185

Electrical Contractors Association (ECA)
Esca House
34 Palace Court
London W2 4HY
Tel: 071-229 1266

Fire Extinguishing Trades Association (FETA)
48a Eden Street
Kingston upon Thames
Surrey KT1 1EE
Tel: 081-549 8839

Fire Protection Association
140 Aldersgate Street
London EC1A 4HX
Tel: 071-606 3757

Fire Research Station
Borehamwood
Hertfordshire WD6 2BL
Tel: 081-207 5299

Fire Resistant Glass and Glazed Systems Association (FRGGSA)
15a Duke Street
Princes Risborough
Buckinghamshire HP17 0AT
Tel: 0844 275500

Guild of Architectural Ironmongers
8 Stepney Green
London E1 3JU
Tel: 071-790 3431

Health and Safety Executive
Baynards House
1 Chepstow Place
Westbourne Grove
London W2 4FT
Tel: 071-243 6000

HMSO Publications Centre
St Crispins
Duke Street
Norwich NR3 lPD
Tel: Enquiries 0603 622211
Orders: 071 873 0011

Institution of Electrical Engineers (IEE)
Savoy Place
London WC2R 0BL
Tel: 071-240 1871

Institution of Fire Engineers
148 New Walk
Leicester LE1 7QB
Tel: 0533 553654

Intumescent Fire Seals Association (IFSA)
Stocking Lane
Hughenden Valley
High Wycombe
Buckinghamshire HP14 4ND
Tel: 0240 243091

Liquefied Petroleum Gas Industry Technical Association
17 Grosvenor Crescent
London SWlX 7ES
Tel: 0737 224700

Loss Prevention Certification Board
Melrose Avenue
Borehamwood
Herts WD6 2BJ
Tel: 081-207 2345

Loss Prevention Council
140 Aldersgate Street
London EC1A 4HY
Tel: 071-606 1050

National Inspection Council for Electrical Installation Contracting (NICEIC)
Vintage House
37 Albert Embankment
London SE1 7UJ
Admin: 071-582 7746
Technical: 071-735 1322

National Approval Council for Security Systems (NACOS)
Queensgate House
14 Cookham Road
Maidenhead
Berkshire SL6 8AJ

Society of Fire Protection Engineers (UK Chapter)
c/o C.S. Todd & Associates Ltd
74 Crooksbury Road
Runfold
Farnham
Surrey GU10 1QD
Tel: 0251 83484

Society of Fire Safety Engineers
149 London Road
Warrington
Cheshire WA4 6LG
Tel: 0925 415456

Timber Research and Development Association
Stocking Lane
Hughenden Valley
High Wycombe
Buckinghamshire HP14 4ND
Tel: 0240 243091

Unit of Fire Safety Engineering University of Edinburgh
The King's Buildings
Edinburgh EH9 3JL
Tel: 031-667 1081 ext 3616

Index